The Accrington Folly

A story of the town,
a family and an island

George Marshall

ISBN: 1-905621-75-2
ISBN 13: 978-1-905621-75-0

First published in the UK

Pen Press Publishers Ltd
39 Chesham Road
Brighton BN2 1NB

0845 108 0530

www.penpress.co.uk

1

The Photograph

Photography is truth.
Jean-Luc Godard

****

'Where are you going to,' said the man up on the quay.

'We're making for the Island of Rum,' I told him as the mooring lines were brought on board the yacht. I was following the nautical convention for a boat to be 'making for' rather than 'going to' its intended destination, a tradition established when travel on the sea was entirely dependent on the vagaries of natural elements. To arrive anywhere at all was not always assured and the success of a voyage accepted as being beyond the puny powers of solely human agency. The outcome a matter of fate and in the hands of some higher power; it was the wise acceptance that existence itself is of a contingent nature. To be making for Rum avoids the folly of presuming a future arrival — yet this was to be a voyage filled with folly.

I had been to Rum once before, to plant trees, travelling then by car and ferry. When found on the map the island, in soft brown and green set in clear blue, had beckoned beguilingly. Maps shape our view of the world by the ways in which they seek to present reality. Gone are the fabulous beasts and fantastic figures depicted in earlier times but the romance and excitement of maps remains. Such dreams they set in motion — especially of islands, and of small and remote islands with their particular allure. These seem to hold some promise, some magic that lies across the sea, just beyond the horizon. To go to this appealing island and there to plant trees— itself a satisfying and optimistic activity, was an opportunity that could not be resisted.

The sea was grey, the island was black, the wind bitter and the sky dark. Digging through saturated layers of matted grass to plant a tiny oak proved strenuous. The incessant rain ran down the face like tears. Alone it would have been a dispiriting experience but in a jolly group the shared discomfort was laughed at. Trees were planted, friendships started and Scottish Natural Heritage, owners of the island, were happy. And that would have been the end of it if it had not been for the photograph.

A wild place was Rum; the whole island a nature reserve with little evidence of normal habitation, of metalled roads or power lines and of commercial agriculture. An island for nature not people. The few residents directly or indirectly engaged in the work of Scottish Heritage, the arbiters of all activity on Rum and their boat then the only way ashore from the Mallaig ferry. Incongruous within this semi-wilderness imposed a large turreted mansion—Kinloch Castle.

It was during a tour of the Castle that the astonishing connection was made. Up to that point the place had held the usual vague interest of an opulent Edwardian stately home, albeit one in which everything had been left as if one day the occupants had suddenly decided to walk out. And then to come upon the photograph—staring out of which were the sepia faces of the 1920 Accrington Relief Committee. What had this place to do with my home town? Central in the picture was the man whose portrait looked down onto the Great Hall of this, his vast summer residence: the man who had commissioned this painting, Sir George Bullough. Bullough!—of course Howard & Bullough Ltd., manufacturers of textile machinery, once the dominating business in the town. The singular irony of the contrast between the need for poor relief in Accrington and this lavish building—raised out of wealth created in the town—was striking. The curiosity aroused by the persisting image of that photograph is directing this sail boat down the estuary to the sea.

4

Some days after coming across the Relief Committee photograph I was crouched in the lee of some dripping rocks on the mountain top of Hallival: it was a day off from tree planting. True wilderness up here with no paths and few marks of people. We were within cloud which was streaming in from the south-west — to the nautical mind at a steady force seven. Anywhere else it would be considered to be raining, on Rum it could almost pass for a fine day. All that could be seen were rocks and stones but way below by the shore the trees should be taking hold. Breaks began to appear in the cloud cover, the sun broke through and the sea shone up, magical, blue and bewitching. From within a timeless mist the spectral shape of Sir George Bullough's steam yacht loomed briefly down in Loch Scresort. Driven to folly in the moment of this intoxicating sea-going vision I announced to my companion:

'Next time I come to Rum I will sail here in my own boat'.

2

The Folly

The man who lives free from folly is not as wise as he thinks.
La Rouchefoucauld

****

The boat cleared the narrow harbour entrance, its tall white sails filling in the lifting breeze. There were several craft this sparkling summer day moving under sail down the estuary on the ebb tide but no other likely to be heading as far north as the Hebrides. In a freshening wind the boat surged forward on the strengthening ebb. Wallis, the crew, carefully coiled and neatly secured the main halyard. He liked everything to be shipshape, to him sailing was a serious matter. Life too; he had to know the way of things, the reason why. Why decide to sail to a folly and anyway what was a folly? The foolish and fanciful aspect of human beings requiring by Wallis as close an examination and interpretation as an Admiralty Chart. Wallis was happy just to be sailing, making out that the whimsical nature of the cruise was of little consequence to him, yet it had stirred his curiosity. He came back along the deck and sat in the cockpit.

'The dictionary describes a folly as a costly and ornamental building considered as serving no practical purpose,' he informed me, his eyes up on the sails checking their setting.

He was assured that Kinloch Castle qualified in having been extremely costly and extensively ornamented, but it had not been built without purpose. He seemed unimpressed to be told that this voyage was part of a search to discover, not just a decaying building, but of where the source of such folly lay. Yet he was receptive to the idea that much of life is lived in the imagination — the dream world of the awake mind, and that the extent to which imaginings become realisable depends upon the means available. George Bullough built his castle and was also able to afford an ocean-going steam yacht to go round the world whilst we were on a 26 foot sailing cruiser heading for the Hebrides, a difference of scale only. Wallis's interest in the *folie de grandeur* of men now became subsumed by a more immediate concern, pointing out that this sailing cruiser, now beginning to pitch in steeper waves as the estuary opened to the sea, had too much sail on for the increasing wind

The opulent and costly Kinloch Castle was certainly not without purpose, although that purpose might itself be considered fanciful. It was intended, as too the steam yacht *Rhouma*, to substantiate the social advancement of George Bullough. He had inherited Rum and considerable wealth from his father, John Bullough, a dynamic and successful businessman whose inventiveness had brought many improvements to textile machinery. George's only known invention was of himself.

The plunging bow of the boat was now pointing to the sea's horizon, nature's straight edge where the world used to end. From over that horizon, breaking into the static hiss of the boat's radio, came a gale warning from the Coast Guard. Within a few hours the mounting seas were making life on board uncomfortable and shelter had to be sought. It is difficult to advance any rational argument for this form of travel, lacking as it does, any of the attendant comforts enjoyed by George Bullough on his voyages. With a crew of over thirty there was no cause for him to struggle on a canting deck to reef a flogging sail whilst drenched in spray. But pleasure takes many forms and the wet and battered Wallis was smiling.

3

The Town

God made the country, and man made the town.
William Cowper

****

'I've heard of the football team, but where is the place?' Wallis was more familiar with the Indian sub-continent than the industrial north of England. It was time to improve his education and, as it was his spell of steering the boat, he was a captive pupil stuck to the tiller. Here is what I intended to tell him:

The name of the town comes from the Old English 'aecern' and 'tun' — where acorns are found. It did not feature in the Domesday Book, that honour went to nearby Hunicot — the place where honey is collected, which as Huncoat eventually became part of Accrington. These early names give a rosy image of an Anglo-Saxon rustic life of eating pork from pigs fed on acorns and drinking mead made from honey. The agrarian nature of the district continued well into the eighteenth century with its inhabitants engaged in the home spinning and weaving of wool from sheep grazing on the hills. This comfortable rural environment was to be forever changed by the impact of the Industrial Revolution.

Cotton had been woven in Manchester as early as 1641 but only on wool warp as pure cotton cloth was prohibited by statute to protect the wool trade, then the main source of England's wealth. The growing demand for cotton cloth grew, doubtless stimulated by the availability from illicit sources, and in 1774 its production was legalised. The first significant manifestation of the Industrial Revolution locally was the Brookside Printworks in nearby Oswaldtwistle in 1760 and later it was here that spinning jennies were first used. These early examples of mechanisation, invented in 1764 by local man James Hargreaves, enabled thread to be spun onto a large number of spindles instead of just the one of a traditional spinning wheel. The implications of the introduction of these machines were not lost on the workforce and during an angry protest against their use the mob drove Hargreaves from his home. The first factory actually to have been located in Accrington was Broad Oak Printworks in 1782, engaged in printing on calico — white or unbleached cotton cloth. Originally printed calico was imported from India where the patterns were often painted by hand but high tariffs were imposed to protect the developing British industry.

By 1801 Accrington was an expanding industrial village of three thousand people. The first power looms were installed in 1818 and there was a shift from water power to steam using locally mined coal. No longer tied to fast flowing streams mills could now be located more conveniently in the valley bottoms and better able to take advantage of the railway which came in 1848. By this time Accrington would have the appearance of a smoke-hung factory encampment and its River Hyndburn transformed from a pleasant trout stream to an outlet for industrial and domestic effluent. A local Board of Health was established in 1853 to bring about improvements and under which the townships of Old and New Accrington were united. In 1878 the district was incorporated as the Borough of Accrington which existed as a separate entity until 1974 when it was subsumed within the newly created Borough of Hyndburn. In recognition of it being the largest town the new borough coat of arms adopted Accrington's motto but with one significant change: *Industry and Prudence Conquer* became *By Industry and Prudence*. This shift from the forceful and unequivocal assertion by the Victorian forbears to a more tentative guiding principle for the borough reflects a century of changes which have affected the town.

Wallis did not receive this history of Accrington as intended but was given a much more garbled account, interrupted by the need to change a sail and by his own interjections to the narrative. His view was that the Anglo-Saxons had the best of it with their pork and honey, with a home by an unpolluted trout stream in a valley frequented by deer. Not for them a life of labouring in factories. His scepticism about developments considered as representing progress would have made him an ideal Luddite and was perhaps one of the reasons he was happy on a boat driven by the wind.

4

The Gentleman

Pleasure is a thief to business.
Daniel Defoe

****

It would have taken only a fraction of George Bullough's considerable wealth to buy himself the luxurious ocean-going steam yacht. He already had a boat, the 55ft cutter *Mysterie* which had been his father's—but George had much grander ideas. Like his grandfather and father he too had ambitions though these were not to be expressed in the development and manufacture of textile machinery. George aspired to the life and pleasures of an English gentleman and from the time of the death of his father in 1891 applied much of his inherited wealth to this purpose. In this he was following the example of many of those men made rich in the nineteenth century from commerce and industry seeking to emulate the lifestyle of the landed gentry. This model of the desirable life contained within its culture a disapproval of any association with trade or manufacturing, fostering a view that 'new money' so accumulated, however much there was of it, did not confer the established status and prestige of 'old money' derived from longstanding ownership of land and property. It is an attitude thought to have some responsibility for the lack of sustained industrial development in Britain. George, in his keenness to conform to the mores of the admired social class, makes no mention of business interests in his entry to *Who's Who*.

He was born at Accrington in 1870 but, unlike his father who settled there, George's life was to be spent away from the town and to have little direct association with it. His social aspirations, no doubt encouraged by his education at Harrow, were to be accomplished elsewhere. When his father died George had to return from a two-year world cruise which it is suggested this handsome, six foot five inches tall son had been dispatched on because of his developing feelings for his young step-mother. Be that as it may, the widowed Mrs. Bullough married an army colonel the following year. George inherited half the business and the Isle of Rum estate. John (Ion), his half-brother, was to inherit the other fifty percent of the business and the Meggerrie Castle estate in Perthshire when he came of age. Howard and Bullough became a private limited company and later, because of continuing growth, a public company. George, the major shareholder, became chairman in 1904, a position he retained throughout his life.

One of his first acts following his inheritance revealed a desire to disconnect himself from the town. He had his father's body removed from the family vault at Accrington's Christ Church, where the previous generation lay and where there is a memorial window to the grandparents. His father's body was re-interred on Rum where it was to suffer further disturbance in the interests of his son's social aspirations. Apparently the tiled subterranean vault George had constructed was likened to a public urinal by some influential visitor which led George to have an imposing structure built like a Greek temple in classical Doric style overlooking the sea at Harris. There his father's body was taken and his previous resting place blown up. The scope of his ambition became apparent by his purchase of the steam yacht in 1895. An even greater statement of his intention to be seen as one of the society he wished to be part of followed with the ambitious and costly construction of Kinloch Castle.

The Castle was not yet complete when the Boer War broke out in October 1899. George immediately took this opportunity to display his worth to the country and by the end of the year *ss*

Rhouma, with its owner on board, was at anchor in Table Bay. There he placed his boat and its crew at the disposal of the Army as a hospital ship. A wooden structure was built on the afterdeck to accommodate twenty non-commissioned soldiers whilst the cabins and state rooms of this luxurious yacht housed up to fifteen officers. All the patients were convalescing from wounds received in fighting the Boers. After a year, its promotional mission accomplished, *Rhouma* sailed home carrying wounded officers who were to convalesce at the newly completed Kinloch Castle. The war, and the needs of the wounded, continued until May 1902 but by February 1901 the yacht had returned to its civilian role and George was cruising to Madeira with the married daughter of the Fourth Marquis de la Pasture on board. Yet his endeavours had proved sufficient and on 11 December 1901 George Bullough was made a Knight Bachelor by King Edward VII for his patriotic activities in providing for the alleviation of the suffering of British troops.

Monique Lilly de la Pasture/ Ducarel, George's guest on *Rhouma,* was a noted beauty rumoured to have been a mistress of the Prince of Wales and whose father had fled to England to escape from the fate of aristocrats in revolutionary France. At twenty she had married Charles Charrington, a wealthy member of the brewing family. He cited George as co-respondent in divorce proceedings and a month after the decree absolute Monique and George were married on Rum with a reception in grand style at Kinloch Castle on 24th June 1903. The one child of Monique's previous marriage, a daughter, remained with the father.

Sir George was an enthusiastic horseman and combined his enjoyment of riding with the desire for enhancing his social standing by becoming a cavalry officer with the Scottish Horse Imperial Yeomanry. A step up the landed gentry ladder came with his appointment as Master of Ledbury Hounds, his main home then at Ross-on-Wye. He was eventually succeeded in this post by his half-brother Ion who had moved from Meggerrie Castle in 1920 to live in Gloucestershire.

The onset of war in 1914 and the ensuing years of desperate conflict and crushing loss of life, brought fundamental changes to everyday life in Britain. But things were not too bad for Sir George: Howard and Bullough Ltd. was busily engaged in the profitable production of munitions and Sir George was made a baronet in 1916. This further elevation in the social hierarchy was his reward for making an interest free loan of £50,000 to the government. There was also success on the racetrack when his horse *Ballymacad* won the 1917 Grand National.

George's love of horses was of great advantage as racing was the real entrée to the high society of King Edward VII's time and he received the ultimate social accolade when he was elected to the Jockey Club in 1922. Central to this society was Newmarket where he kept a string of racehorses. It was here that George had a large mansion built as his principal residence. In a sale notice Warren Hill House was described in 1986 as 'Newmarket's most luxurious and beautiful house' with a suggested price of over £10,000,000 for it and the associated stud farm. Social acceptance was complete when his only child, Hermione, married Lord Lambton, Fifth Earl of Durham. When George died in July 1939 it was perhaps fittingly in character that he was playing golf in France. His body was taken to Rum and interred in his splendid mausoleum.

5

The Sailing

There is nothing – absolutely nothing – half so much worth doing
as simply messing about in boats.
Wind in the Willows

****

The hubris in that bold announcement on the top of Hallival that one day I would sail to Rum in my own boat would have incited the ire of the Greek gods ever sensitive to the arrogance of humans. It is one of the effects of mountains, that god-like feeling when looking down on the world below, which dismisses any thoughts of nemesis and Rum was where my boat, *Walden Three,* riding the restless waters of the Irish Sea, was now heading. Many and varied are the craft which have approached the island, very few of whose occupants would have done so in the sublime spirit of Kenneth Grahame's riverbank rodent. Back in the eighth millennium B.C. came Mesolithic people in their frail craft of animal skins, risking the waves in the compelling search for sources of food. Thousands of years later would come passing an expedition of Agricola's Roman galleys round the north of Scotland. After 798 AD, when Iona was plundered, came the threatening Viking longships, their ferocious crews intent on pillage.

The Norsemen's power over the Hebrides stemmed from their seamanship and the superior technology of the longship. This power was not successfully challenged until 1188 when Somerled, founder of Clan Donald, won a great sea battle off the coast of

Islay with his fleet of birlinns. These Highland Galleys were derived from longships, but swifter and more manoeuvrable as the earlier steering oar had been replaced by a rudder. Somerled's descendants built hundreds of birlinns and with them ruled their kingdom of islands. The significance of these notable craft in the life of island communities is expressed by the frequent representation of them on gravestones and a memory of them is also preserved on the Oban coat of arms.

The inhabitants of Rum are likely to have seen remnants of the defeated Spanish Armada struggling back home and they came to be directly affected by this failed invasion. At nearby Mull, somewhere in the mud of Tobermory Bay, is the wreck of the galleon *San Juan Bautista* which limped into the Bay in 1588. There are various stories of this encounter between the Spaniards and the locals. One has it that MacLean of Duart, in return for provisions, was given the services of a hundred Spanish marines from the ship who he then used to attack and pillage Rum and the other Small Isles. Such internecine warfare was a feature of clan society and persisted until the suppression of the clan structure following the Battle of Culloden in 1745. Dispute arose with the Spaniards about the terms of the agreement and one of MacLean's men, held on board as hostage, set fire to the ship which blew up and sank. There is the belief that the ponies of Rum and the other Western Isles are descended from those carried by the Armada although, as with so many beguiling myths, it is belied by the facts which insist that most of the pack animals were mules and anyway all livestock was dumped overboard off Eastern Scotland to save water.

The English Civil War did not leave the area untouched. Many Royalist clansmen fought and were captured at the Battle of Worcester in 1651. Cromwell's response, in an early example of gunboat diplomacy, was to send a man-of-war to harry the Hebrides in order to deter men from ever again enlisting in the Royalist cause. Later, during the Commonwealth's war with Scotland, English naval ships were active in the area, one of which has been discovered on the sea-bed in the Sound of Mull. Long after England's short-lived republic the present Queen, on a Hebridean cruise, is said to have come ashore on Rum from the Royal Yacht *Britannia* to picnic at the secluded Kilmory beach.

Unlike earlier boats no warlike intent or need of food was impelling *Walden Three*'s passage north. The very notion of having a sail boat capable of crossing the sea to distant islands had come suddenly and unexpectedly. The first of two epiphanic moments, contradictory in their revelations, connected with sailing. In childhood messing about in boats had been limited to summer holidays in the Lake District desperately attempting to enact, in hired rowing boats on Lake Windermere and Coniston Water, the sailing adventures of Arthur Ransome's privileged children: Nancy Blackett, captain of the *Amazon*, then and still, my girl hero. The possibility of actually sailing, of learning to sail let alone having a boat, was too remote to even contemplate. But the desire must have been implanted and, as with seeds that await the right conditions in which to germinate, for many years lay dormant. The temptation is to say it had to await a mid-life crisis, an over used term that blocks and absolves closer examination of a particular situation. For life as it is lived, and not when considered in retrospect, is throughout composed of a sequence of crises.

The sailing seed eventually blossomed into the fresh white hull and red sails of a small dinghy; at last a craft to be carried by wind alone on waters where the *Swallow* and rival *Amazon* had tacked and jibed! Those lingering Ransome ghosts were quickly dispelled in the sheer exuberance of a vibrant boat skimming over the glittering waters of a wind livened lake. Surely there was nothing better in life than this? And for a time there was not. The idea of having a sea-going boat had never existed in the mind even dormantly, and besides there was something awesome about the open sea. Any prospect of encountering the violence of the sea in a small boat was frightening and fortunately was not something that was likely be confronted as a dinghy sailor. A move was made from lake to sea but only onto the sheltered waters of an estuary.

The revelation came on one of those warm, blue-skied days that are the memory of summer time. A friend and I were jilling about in the dinghy on the estuary when the dock gates opened and out came a procession of sailing cruisers. I'd noticed boats going out before but had never watched them from off the water; never with this urgent desire to follow them out to the shimmering silver horizon that beckoned.

'That's what I want to do,' I said. 'Go out there.' And gazed longingly after the yachts heading into a luminous perfection of sea and sky. Such folly! But that alluring vision of the open sea, that last wilderness, remained vivid and, not only proved resistant to any inroads of rationality, but in the pursuit of its realisation became an obsession.

On a cold December day I clambered aboard *Walden Three* and was immediately transported. Sitting in the cockpit there came the feeling of her lifting serenely to the waves as the azure sea slid past; overhead I saw tall sails, white as swans, billowing in bright sunshine. The cosy cabin held the promise of snug nights swinging gently in quiet anchorages. The boat was laid up for the winter and lying ashore in North Wales, shiny and for sale. Her 26 foot length would absorb a far greater proportion of financial resources than George Bullough used to invest in the 221 feet of *Rhouma.* For him it was truly an investment, his steam yacht a necessary accoutrement for his social advance. The main purpose of *Walden Three,* although the boat did not then have this name, was to allow indulgence in the romantic fancy of sailing over the sea.

There was another fantasy relating to the boat and this is revealed in her re-naming: that life on board would embody the best of two conflicting utopian concepts. One derived from Henry Thoreau's *Walden*; his account in 1854 of living simply and in touch with nature ('we need the tonic of wildness') is an anarchistic rejection of what he saw were the wrongs of society. The other concept coming from the behaviourist psychologist B. F. Skinner's riposte to Thoreau in his book *Walden Two* (1948) in which he describes his idea of an idealised society which would 'induce people to adopt new ways of living which are less consuming'.

Wherever we go in this small and densely populated island we are walking on history. The derelict harbour on whose quay *Walden Three* was sitting had once been a thriving port through which many thousands of tons of Welsh slate passed. This memory deepened the silence of the place. One of its ghosts was the husband of a woman I had once lodged with in the town; a man who had spent his life working at the harbour. He had reached a supervisory position, directing operations from the shelter of a wooden hut, a shelter that the management removed after he became active in the union. His wife was convinced that his early death was due to the ensuing years of having to stand out in the cold and the wet.

Walden Three chugged out of this darkened Welsh harbour one chilly April night with its novice skipper and volunteer crew of innocents. This first passage, a consequence of the reckless desire to bring the boat home, was one of the wildest experienced, its folly exposed on the windswept waters of the Irish sea. Yet quickly forgotten next day when the sun shone, the wind eased, the sea calmed and the crew recovered. The voyage to Rum not yet in the offing.

6

The Shipmate

Chance governs all.
Paradise Lost

****

Two of us were on a six-berth yacht off the Turkish coast. This was a 'potluck' flotilla sailing package where you take a chance on who else will be sharing the boat. Luckily there had not been enough people to crowd the boat to capacity but perhaps I was not so fortunate in the man allocated as my shipmate. I didn't know what to make of my new companion; he was not very talkative and volunteered little about himself. The entire flotilla consisted of only two other craft; one of these with three newly acquainted men on board, the other with a young couple employed as the flotilla leaders. After a couple of hours of keen sailing these 'leaders' were left some way astern of their charges.

'OK, you guys — you obviously don't need us.' Came the voice over the radio.

We were free to sail how and where we pleased. The other designated skipper, a bronzed Australian who drank the fiery raki neat, agreed that we would meet up at various times as we sailed along the coast. I had a feeling that I would need some convivial encounters with him and his crew as there seemed little prospect of much interesting and stimulating conversation from my shipmate. Wallis, for it was he, had little actual sailing experience but was well versed in the theory and technicalities of his new-found hobby and had brought several sailing manuals with him. He was keen to learn the practicalities of sailing although his careful and deliberate approach was at times frustrating when the situation required a degree of urgency. But he bore my impatient demands with a stolid acceptance.

A few days into the holiday we were sailing along the coast looking for a taverna or any place where there was the prospect of a cooling beer but this thickly wooded section seemed uninhabited. Then it appeared—a table and some empty chairs by the sea edge in a small bay. The anchor was let go in water clear as air and a line from the stern was secured ashore, Mediterranean style. The glistening white yacht, afloat on its lucent image, dazzling in the sun's glare.

We headed for the table and the waiting chairs. Above them, nailed to the trunk of the shading tree, was a wooden board on which were two simple drawings: one of a chicken and one of a fish. We sat down and saw up through the trees a dwelling of sorts dug into the hillside. A man came out of it, stooping under the low doorway, a tall, thin man dressed in the loose clothing of the country people. A man with a wide, welcoming smile greeting us like brothers. The words he used were unintelligible as were ours to him. There was little need of them to sense that here was a man happy with his abode in the hillside and content with his collection of chairs gathered beneath a tree.

He sat opposite us at the wooden table, smiling his pleasure at our presence. He made a drinking gesture and, in response to nods, sped up the hill. Our host returned with bottles of beer and cola which he proudly displayed on the rough table. He would not have a drink himself but sat smiling encouragement and sharing our enjoyment of his beer. The wine-dark sea of Homer, at this time of day more sapphire than claret, lapped at our feet and shimmered away to the horizon. There was an aroma of pine; a cracking from heated trees; bursts of cicada chorus— and more beer.

We pointed to the fish outline on the tree notice. Our host lost his smile and sadness showed in his eyes. 'No fish?' 'No feesh,' he confirmed, empty hands turned outwards in dismay. We were joined at the table by the family; a girl and a boy, aged around five or six, and their mother whose dark beauty had resisted the rigours of her existence. Come to see the foreigners from the white yacht and to share in the occasion. They sat close alongside the father, arms around one another, mirroring his smile, their eyes curious. The expensive white yacht with its tall silvered mast loomed like a threat to such blessedness.

It was time to eat and the chicken drawing on the wooden menu was indicated. The whole family enthusiastically affirmed its availability. They left together stepping under the sun-dappling trees up to their woodland home. A white sail appeared around the headland barely moving in the still air. My fellow skipper was here! I waved him into the bay and gave the family to understand there were extra orders for chicken. The Aussie arrived accompanied by one of his crew.

'Bloody Hell!' Was his reproachful response to our venue. He said they were on their way further down the coast where there was a real bar and a restaurant—a proper place. He was given time to sink a few beers before being told this is where he was eating, the meal already being prepared. Up by the family dwelling smoke was rising from an outdoor oven. From its vicinity came a desperate squawking and figures were darting between trees. Without any warning Wallis leapt off his chair and rushed up through the trees. We watched in astonishment as he joined in the chase for the condemned fowl and was able to grab the bird. He held it up by the legs in one hand and was in the act of dispatching it by dislocating its neck by the other. He was halted by a gesture of disapproval by its owner who was obviously worried by the prospect of such alien slaughter. Wallis, respecting the requirements of Islam, handed back the chicken for ritual killing. He returned to his chair with a rare smile on his face. It was the first but not the last time I would be surprised by this man.

The chicken came to us on four plates with a salad of home grown tomatoes. Sure it was tough, I agreed with my Aussie pal, but it had been quite a sprinter. We chewed diligently, closely observed by the attentive family. On a scrap of paper the father produced some figures, a ridiculously small sum. We paid our grateful friend the amount he had written and then pressed notes into the hands of the children. There seemed a reluctance to see us go. Leaving in the sleek yacht we waved to the family, sitting yet at the table in the darkening shadow of their tree.

That night we ate at the Australian's intended restaurant. From the sea it was a string of coloured lights along the shore. There was a new jetty and a wooden walkway; a hubbub of voices and Western pop music came from the bar. The owner, smoothly suited, perspiration showing on his forehead, greeted us in excellent English. The menu was extensive. I have no memory of what we ate.

7

The Grandfather

There is no such thing as Society.
There are individual men and women, and there are families.
Margaret Thatcher

****

George never knew his grandfather who died two years before George was born. It seems unlikely that James Bullough, the originating Bullough of the business, would have approved of his grandson's way of life. The contrast with his own, in which at the age of seven he was operating a handloom, would have been too great to envisage. He was born in 1799 at Westhoughton at a time when most weaving in Lancashire was still done by families in the home. Yet this established way of life was already becoming threatened by the impact of industrialisation and the expansion of steam-powered factory production. It was a time of uncertainty, strife and social disruption.

With cheap cloth came violence from people made desperate from loss of their livelihood. The Luddites have been demonised as anarchic opponents of technological developments but the Luddite machine breaking in 1812 was not only by impoverished handloom weavers. Many of the riots were by factory workers reacting directly against starvation wages. The *Leeds Mercury* commented at the time on the discipline of the workers who only targeted the machines of owners who had lowered wages. Machine breaking did not start with the Luddites and must have been a feature of an earlier period judging by the reaction of the government which made it a capital offence as long ago as 1721. Many of the 'Luddite' rioters were sentenced to death although in most cases this was commuted to transportation.

James Bullough's birthplace did not escape the effects of the rioters as in 1812 the machines in Westhoughton Mill were smashed, an event likely to have been seen by the young James. But his future was to be within the burgeoning industrialisation of cloth production and, by 1824 when he married, he had been employed in a supervisory capacity as an overlooker at factories in Bury and Bolton. The following year he was managing a small factory although his inventive mind still engaged in improving handlooms and resulted in the Dandy Loom, a much more efficient machine.

But the outlook for handloom weavers was bleak; in 1800 an average weekly wage was 27 shillings, in 1815 it was down to15 shillings and had fallen to 8 shillings by 1820, and this decline continued. In April 1826 John Lancaster, secretary of Blackburn Weavers Union, wrote to the Home Secretary, Robert Peel:

Our dwellings are totally destitute of every necessary comfort, every article of value has disappeared either to satisfy the cravings of hunger or to appease the clamour of relentless creditors: our homes, where plenty and contentment once resided, are now become the abodes of penury and wretchedness. Thousands who were once possessed of an honest independence gained by laborious industry, are now sunk in the lowest depths of poverty.

This impassioned appeal for intervention by the government, which goes on to cite the power loom as the cause of their distress, went unheeded and later that month there were outbreaks of power loom breaking in different parts of the county. Near Accrington a group of about 1,000 men and women, many armed with pikes, cudgels and sledgehammers, gathered on Whinney Hill and marched to a mill at Higher Grange Lane where they demolished 60 looms. In the next few days power looms were smashed at mills in several Lancashire towns but Preston, where James Bullough was now employed as an overlooker at Rodgett's Cotton Mill, seems to have escaped. The government sent in the military and at Chadderton riflemen opened fire on the crowd, killing six people and wounding many more.

The Powerloom Riots of 1826 were a final outpouring of protest by Lancashire handloom weavers in their fight for survival and they were over by the end of the month. Many of those who took part were rounded up and imprisoned. Twenty-seven men and six women, sentenced at Lancaster Assizes, were hanged for their involvement. Several others were transported for life. The mill owners did not suffer as they were compensated by the local authorities from money levied on already poverty-stricken households. The power looms were soon repaired and running again and the demise of the handloom weaver continued unabated.

Handlooms now being a thing of the past James Bullough's inventiveness became focussed on the improvement of power looms. He had moved to employment at Brookhouse Mills in Blackburn where he and his associate, William Kenworthy, in 1841 jointly patented devices known as the Roller Temple and Weft Fork. Production from the improved looms was at a time of depression in the industry and their introduction was resisted by a workforce fearful that their use would result in further reductions in employment. In August 1842 groups of protesters went from mill to mill in several towns immobilising the new looms by knocking out the plugs of the steam boilers. James Bullough, at the forefront of the hated technological developments, was forced to leave Blackburn for a time during this period of what came to be known as the Plug-Drawing Riots.

James finally went into the cotton business on own account and by 1850 was trading as James Bullough and Son at Shoe Mill, Baxenden, with 70 employees operating 75 looms. It was in Baxenden that he had his home for the rest of his life living modestly in the end house of a street of houses he had built for his workers. In 1856 he went into partnership with John Howard, an engineer who had established a small loom making business at Accrington, and in 1856 the firm of Howard and Bullough was born. His youngest son, John, joined the company in 1862.

This was at the time of the 'cotton famine' brought about by the outbreak of the American Civil War the previous year and the subsequent Federal blockade of the southern ports. Many were out of work because of the shortage of cotton and had to survive on poor relief and soup kitchens. In spite of the widespread distress a meeting of cotton workers on 31st December 1862 at the Free Trade Hall in Manchester pledged their support for the Federal fight to abolish slavery, a declaration which elicited an address of thanks from Abraham Lincoln.

James became the sole owner of Howard and Bullough when his partner died in 1866 and on his own death in July 1868 was succeeded by his son, John.

8

The Successor

Industry and Prudence Conquer.
Accrington Coat of Arms

****

'He bought the whole island?' Wallis, who had never been to the Hebrides, was incredulous. He looked across the white-flecked waves to where the Isle of Man stretched for thirty miles across the near horizon from the Point of Ayre to Langness. The substantial town of Douglas, a location of international finance, prominent in summer sunshine. An island conveniently situated in the middle of the Irish Sea; convenient in the past for smugglers and convenient in the present for offshore money. Home to tax exiles who endure its limitations for the health of their bank balance. Rum was much different, Wallis was informed.

Markedly different too was John Bullough's upbringing from that of his father who is reputed to have worn clogs throughout his working life. Although the youngest son his abilities had earmarked him as the one to succeed his father in the business and he was given the benefit of an education at Queenswood College, Hampshire, which under Quaker influence had become a centre of scientific learning. From there he went on to study at Glasgow University before joining the family firm. At the age of 31 John inherited a thriving business with 300 employees producing cotton spinning and weaving machinery at Globe Works, Accrington. He also inherited an inventive mind and an enterprising attitude but differed from his father in having a more outgoing nature, involving himself in politics and becoming a public figure.

John's astute commercial sense led him to a decision in 1876 that had a profound effect on the future of Howard and Bullough. He decided to exhibit the company's new carding machine at the American Centennial Exhibition in Philadelphia. This machine won an award but it was another machine that was to transform the future of Howard and Bullough. Whilst there John saw a new type of spindle which he realised could revolutionise spinning. He bought the rights from the inventor and the machine tools for its production were shipped over to Accrington. Production of the Rabbeth Ring Spindle began at Globe Works in 1878. This was a year of difficult trading in the industry and the Textile Employers Federation proposed a 10% reduction in wages which led to angry cotton workers burning down the Clayton-le-Dale house of its chairman. There were no such problems at Howard and Bullough as the Rabbeth machine was an immediate success bringing about a massive expansion of the business. Within a few years many thousands had been sold at home and abroad.

John Bullough married Bertha Schmidlin, the daughter of a Swiss cotton manufacturer, in 1869 and his son George was born on 28th February the following year. The family home was then The Laund, Baxenden, and later the larger Rhyddings Hall, Oswaldtwistle.The marriage ended in some kind of scandal and divorce. When he re-married in 1884, to the nineteen year old daughter of a Stornoway banker, the marriage took place at Meggernie Castle in Perthshire on the 50 square-mile estate he had recently purchased. Earlier he had rented the shooting rights of Rum and in 1886 bought the island for £35,000.

The purchase of Rum by John Bullough could never have been justified in any business sense. True it was fashionable and prestigious to acquire a Scottish estate but he already possessed one in Perthshire. This hard-headed business man was not without a streak of romanticism which was probably nurtured by his time at Glasgow University where he studied the arts. Perhaps he was susceptible to the romantic allure of islands, intensified in Rum's case by its association with Lord Salisbury, a man he much admired There is no doubting John's poetic nature and his interest in poetry. His affection for Rum, and an insight into a personality at odds with the accepted sensibilities of a northern industrialist, is seen in the verse of a poem he wrote:

> There's a land in the West
> Tis the isle I love best;
> There the lordly stag doth roam
> And the eagle makes his home.

John was also notable for his patronage of the Lancashire poet, Edwin Waugh, the son of a Rochdale shoemaker. Waugh, who was born in 1817, was employed by a local bookseller and educated himself from the books with which he was surrounded. He became a full-time writer of poetry and prose in both dialect and standard English. His famous Lancashire dialect poem is about weaving work, *The Little Doffer*:

> A merry little doffer lad
> C'oom down to Shapper's Mill,
> To see if he could get a shop;
> He said his name wur ' Bill'.

> 'Bill what,my lad?' th'o'erlooker said;
> 'Arta co'de nought beside?'
> 'Oh yigh,'said th'lad; 'they co'n me things-
> Sometimes,-at's bad to bide!'

> 'But what's thi faither's name, my lad?
> Thou'll surely tell me that!'
> Said th'lad,'Some co'n him Apple Dad,
> His gradely name's Owd Hat.'

'My uncle Joe's co'de Flopper Chop!
An sometimes Owd Betide!
They co'n him thoose at weighvin'-shops;
An I know nought beside.'

Said th'o'erlooker, 'I know owd Joe,
He weighvs for Billy Grime,
But, what dun they co'n thee, my lad,
When they co'n at dinner-time?'

Th'lad grinned an said, 'They never han
To co' me then, no fear!'
Said th'o'erlooker, 'How's that, my lad?'
Said th'lad, 'I'm al'ays theer!'

'My lad, thou looks a lively cowt,
Keen as a cross-cut saw;
Short yure, sharp teeth, a twinklin' e'e
An a little hungry maw!'

'But wheer hasto bin worchin' at?
What's brought tho down our way?'
Said th'lad, 'I wortched for Tommy Platt,
He'gan me th'bag, today.'

'Thou's brought thi character, I guess?'
Says th'lad, 'Yo're wrang, I doubt;'
Says th'o'erlooker to th'lad, 'How's this?'
Says th'lad, 'I'm better bowt!'

Said th'o'erlooker, 'I never see
Such a welp sin I wur born!
But, I'll try what I can make o' thee:
Come to thi wark tomorn!'

Many of his non-dialect poems are expressions of his love of moorland and he is commemorated by Waugh's Well, a stone structure built at a spring on one of his favourite Lancashire moors. He was a man with a social awareness, no doubt arising from his impoverished childhood, and he wrote many reports and essays on social and economic issues affecting Lancashire working people. Yet any differences in political outlook between himself and John Bullough do not appear to have affected their friendship which had Waugh visiting Rum as John's guest. But then John was not a man of narrow interests and who, on the one hand would fund the building of the Accrington Conservative Club would also pay for the publication of an anthology of poems by the Accrington poet, Matilde Harrison, unable herself to afford such a step.

Although he was spending more time in the Highlands John was not neglecting the business. Between 1868 and 1888 he took out 26 patents in his own name and was joint patentee in many more. He had also shown himself to have a progressive approach to labour relations and displayed in Kinloch Castle is an open letter of 1871 from the workforce expressing:

their heartfelt thanks for the very handsome manner in which you have given us unsolicited, the boon of fifty-four hours working time to constitute a week's work without reducing our wages. In thus placing yourself at the head of the movement for abridging the hours of labour in this locality you have performed a service which merits the thanks of every working man in Accrington.

Under his direction Howard and Bullough became the largest manufacturer of ring spinning frames and ring weft frames in the world and employed over 2000 people in Accrington.

John Bullough was a prominent local figure, vociferous in his support of the Conservative Party and he delivered many public speeches expressing his strong political opinions. He became chairman of the local party and was selected to stand for parliament but later withdrew because of his business commitments. He helped found the Accrington Mechanics Institution and gave financial support to local cricket, football and swimming clubs. This energetic and enterprising man was given little time to enjoy the benefits of his wealth as his health began to deteriorate. In early 1891 he and his family set out for Monte Carlo in the hope that the Mediterranean climate would enable him to recover from a lung infection but his condition deteriorated on the way and he died, at the early age of 53, in the Metropole Hotel, London.

Crowds greeted the arrival of John's body at Accrington railway station on 27th February 1891 and the funeral procession to Christ Church passed through streets lined with townspeople. The funeral service took place in a church packed to capacity with many hundreds standing outside. His body was interred in the family vault alongside his parents.

9

The Pals

Red lips are not so red
As the stained stones kissed by the English dead.
Wilfred Owen *Greater Love*

****

The heyday of Kinloch Castle was brief, coinciding with the so-called 'golden' Edwardian era which came to an abrupt end in 1914. There is no greater human folly than warfare and no war was more senseless than that which became known as the Great War, its magnitude hardly diminished by time or in coming to be referred to as WW1, as though it were merely the first of a whole series. Accrington is not unique in its association with the particular lunacy of this conflict but local circumstances have ensured that its name has become attached to one of its most insane incarnations. The town has come to epitomise the grotesque futility of that war, this distinction arising from the events of 1st July, 1916 near the River Somme. At 7.20am 700 men advanced into rifle and machine gun fire, by 8.00am 584 were killed, wounded or missing. Officially they were the 11th(Service) Battalion (Accrington) East Lancashire Regiment but came to be known and remembered as the Accrington Pals.

When the war started on 4th August 1914 the textile industry was in decline and Accrington was in the throes of industrial unrest. The management of Howard and Bullough had refused to give union recognition to the Amalgamated Society of

Engineers or to accede to their request for a minimum wage of 36 shillings (£1.80) for a 53 hour week. On 2nd July 600 engineers went on strike and six days later the management locked out the whole workforce of 5,000. This continued throughout August and the dispute became linked to the war as shown by a letter in the Accrington Observer & Times on 29th August:

Men of Bullough's, what are you doing in this time of stress and trial? Shall I tell you the plain and unvarnished truth? You are daily wasting bright golden hours in registering yourselves at your clubhouse. You are sitting on your heels on the kerbstones twiddling your thumbs. You are propping up the railings of the Ambulance Hall. You are trapesing aimlessly through the already too crowded streets. You are lounging, sitting and standing near the war office in Dutton Street discussing tactics and methods of a warfare in which you will not, either with hammer or gun, play your part for the honour of your country.

In the same issue was a letter from Lady Louise Selina Maxwell with an impassioned appeal for Englishmen to take up arms for their country. Also in this issue was a letter from 'A Patriot' promoting the idea that Accrington, like some other towns, should raise its own local volunteers. Two days later the mayor, Captain John Harwood, contacted the War Office with an offer to raise half a battalion, subsequently raised to a full battalion of 1,100 men.

There was an immediate and pressing need to increase the size of the Army and Lord Kitchener and the War Council, of which the MP for Accrington, Harold Baker, was a member, became convinced that men would be encouraged to enlist if they knew they would serve with friends in 'Pals' battalions. Recruiting of men between the age of 19 and 35 began on 12th September and within three hours over100 men had enlisted, with many more rejected as not meeting the minimum height requirement of 5ft 6in and chest measurement of 35.5in. This was soon reduced to 5ft 3in and 34in in order to speed up recruitment. By 24th September, with the addition of men from Burnley, Blackburn, Great Harwood and a contingent from

Chorley, the battalion was complete, its officers recruited from prominent local men and their families.

At first there was little change from civilian life for these volunteers as they were not in barracks with most billeted in their own homes and training and drilling locally. In February 1915 the battalion was dispatched to Caernarvon, leaving to a magnificent send-off by the town. The Pals did not leave the country until December 1915 and then not for France but to Egypt to guard the Suez Canal. They eventually arrived in France in March 1916. During the next few months they had experience of static trench warfare but July 1st was the first time the Pals were engaged in an all out attack. It was also to be their last as a characteristically Accrington Pals unit. An observer described the lines of dead as being like 'swathes of cut corn at harvest time'. Afterwards at the camp behind the lines there is a report of 'men dribbling in in a terrible state'.

The impact of such fatalities and woundings within a small community had a devastating effect on the town. The local paper was full of photographs of the dead and missing and there were drawn blinds in nearly every street; the bell at Christ Church tolled all day. The Pals unit was reconstituted but never with the same emphasis on local content as the higher command, still persisting in its war of attrition and high casualties, wished to avoid the adverse effect of similar local concentrations of grief. The earlier enthusiasm to volunteer had passed as the reality of modern warfare had made itself felt and, from January 1916, conscription became the means of replacing the dead and maimed. But Accrington was not all gloom, Howard and Bullough, now producing munitions, was busy and profitable again.

10

The Voyage

Nae man can tether time or tide.
Robert Burns *Tam O' Shanter*

****

This long promised voyage to Rum, now underway, almost foundered the previous year at latitude 39 degrees north: longitude 28 degrees west. This is an approximate position as it was arrived at without the aid of satellite navigation but by dead reckoning. The 'dead' not implying something inherently fatal in this method but derived from the 'ded' of deduced reckoning which is based on speed, time and tidal currents. The position was midway between Dublin and the Isle of Man and where no navigational hazard is to be found on the chart. I was returning from having satisfied an ambition, a whim it was, to sail *Walden Three* over to Ireland for a pint of Guinness. For hours we had been out of sight of land and moving slowly over a huge and empty sea. The immensity of sea and sky was elemental and inducive to meditation about life. It was then that I knew I was not going to be one of those yachtsman fully committed to a lifetime of sailing.

Wallis was unaware of this revelation of the previous year and in the excitement of departure there was no feeling of this being a final sail in *Walden Three* and my eagerness to step ashore on Rum to satisfy the curiosity about Kinloch Castle was undiminished. In fact the wish to learn more had intensified as the Bullough family connection stirred up feelings of nostalgia about a childhood in which 'Bullough's' was the defining industry of the town. It was an institution, like the Town Council or the Corporation bus service, whose existence was taken for granted as a permanent and intrinsic fact of life. It was the place where the fathers of my friends had spent their working lives. The idea that it would one day cease to exist, as would those other institutions, did not enter one's thoughts.

In more ways than one John Bullough provided the basis for his son's future folly, his romantic idealisation of Rum reflected in George's desire to impose an exotic fantasy world on the island. Romanticism lies at the bottom of such extravagant folly even when, as in George's case, there was a strong social motivation. It is also a romantic folly, and truly ironic, to go to sound out folly from a yacht, an irrational form of transport in the twenty-first century. An example of using another's folly as an excuse for one's own! But there had been that pledge made on the summit of Halival to return to Rum under sail.

It was a promise I began to regret ever having made the night we hit the tidal race off the Mull of Galloway, the southern extremity of that hammer-headed peninsula. The transformation was sudden and shocking; from the regular movement of the boat in moderate and predictable waves to its leaping and bucking in great gouts of water that lifted up from the sea at random. The boat was slewed this way and that as Wallis, taken unawares at the helm, fought to maintain some kind of control in this powerful ebb tide pouring out of the Solway Firth. The initial anxiety subsided as *Walden Three* showed that she was quite capable of coping with these conditions but it was replaced by a growing feeling of nausea induced by these wild gyrations. After the first exclamations of alarm no words were exchanged and I wondered if I had gone as green as Wallis. It is at such times that I am at one with Shakespeare's Gonzalo in the *Tempest* who would 'give a thousand furlongs of sea for an acre of barren ground; long heath, brown furze, any thing:'.

When eventually through the exhausting tide race and back

in the more usual turbulence of the Irish Sea, it was agreed that we would put into Portpatrick to enable both of us to get some sleep. Portpatrick owes its existence to the proximity of Ireland visible just twenty miles away across the North Channel. It was the original short sea crossing for ferries and mail packet boats, its harbour located at the only feasible gap in the cliffs of this rugged coast. On negotiating the narrow entrance and avoiding the underwater rocks it was easy to see why it was supplanted by Stranraer round in Loch Ryan when there came the need for larger ferries.

Walden Three, its crew refreshed and renewed by hours of undisturbed slumber, came out of Portpatrick into ideal sailing conditions. They did not last; no sailor expects benign conditions to last; perfect sailing like perfect happiness comes rarely. We were comfortably on course for the Mull of Kyntyre when there came an announcement from Clyde Coastguard of an imminent gale. Would there be time to round this notorious headland, now in sight, before the gale was on us? Our 'bible', the *Clyde Cruising Club Sailing Directions*, was not encouraging:

The passage round the Mull of Kyntyre is one which requires great care owing to the tremendous seas which arise in the race off Deas Point when wind and tide are opposed. Conditions can deteriorate rapidly and the timing of the passage is most important. A small craft unless provided with a watertight cockpit and means for battening securely all hatches should not attempt this passage except in settled weather.

This, from the usually matter-of-fact publication, was more than sufficient to swing the decision in favour of heading for the safety of Cambeltown Harbour. Three frustrating days were spent hanging around the bars of this dour town whilst a succession of gales blew themselves out. Nelson's remark that 'men and ships rot in port' was in danger of becoming a depressing reality when finally the winds eased. At the Mull the seas had calmed but sudden swirls and strange movements of water gave an air of foreboding to the place and it was a relief to put this grim headland astern and press on to Ghigha Island.

There, in Ardminish Bay, the anchor rattled down into still, clear water, visible as it lay on the sea bed. A soft silence descended and there was a feeling of having arrived in the Hebrides.

A sublime sail up the magnificent Sound of Jura took us past Barnhill, the isolated house at the extreme north of Jura where George Orwell wrote *1984* and where he chose to spend his final days. For a man suffering from tuberculosis to decide to live in such isolation and in cold, damp accommodation suggests the action of someone determined to die. But today the three Paps of Jura were bathed in warm sunshine and the conditions under which Orwell expressed his pessimistic and bleak view of humanity seemed a world away.

The need to replace an impeller for the engine cooling system forced a diversion to the boatyard in Loch Melfort. The shortest route from here to Rum is through Cuan Sound, a narrow channel between two islands. The sailing directions spoke of fast tides and having to negotiate a gap between two rocks where there was a dangerous eddy.

'Between Scylla and Charybdis,' I explained to Wallis as we entered the Sound.

'They are not rocks ,' he said.

'The original rock and a hard place,' I insisted.

'Scylla is a monster who happens to live on a rock. She has six heads and each reaches down to snatch a member of the crew of passing boats.' Wallis rarely argued over matters of opinion but would not hesitate to correct what he perceived to be factual error.

'And the other one?'

'Charybdis lives on the sea bed opposite Scylla and creates a vortex that sucks boats to the bottom.'

'She must be down there,' I said.

Just ahead was a rapidly circulating rim of white water whose hissing and surging could easily be imagined as the thrashings of some malignant sea monster. Of Scylla there was no sign; her rock was below the surface. *Walden Three,* unscathed and without any loss of crew, was carried as if on a fast flowing river between the rocky shores of the tight channel and out on the tidal stream into the wide waters of the Firth of Lorne. From this seaward continuation of the geological fault splitting Scotland there was an exalted feeling of looking into the very heart of the Highlands away up along the Great Glen. But that was not our destination.

11

The Island

The interior is one heap of rude mountains scarcely possessing an
acre of level land. It is the wildest and repulsive of all islands.
John MacCulloch
The Highlands and Islands of Scotland (1824)

****

Rum is, as Wallis had been informed, indeed a much different place than the Isle of Man but not the dire island as described by Mr. MacCulloch. A man who had obviously not succumbed to the romantic notions of wild countryside then gaining a fashionable hold on the imagination of the English chattering classes influenced by the likes of William Wordsworth. Yet MacCulloch's view is one reflecting the reality of the island as a place of marginal prospects for bountiful habitation. Even so there were people living on Rum eight thousand years ago as the stone tools found there have been dated at around 6,600 B.C. and there is evidence of even earlier Mesolithic settlement at the head of Loch Scresort.

Askival, Hallival, Trallaval; the mountain names resonate in their Norseness as do most of the prominent features which would appear as essential landmarks seen from the deck of a Viking longship. The island name itself probably has Norse origins but there is no evidence of significant Viking settlement even though Rum was in an area of Norse control until the twelfth century. Creag nan Stearnain, Tigh Bhralie, Gualann na Pairc; and other Gaelic names are widely used for aspects of the terrain not relevant to Viking navigation indicating that the resident population has been of Celtic origin. Norse control was replaced by that of the Lordship of the Isles which persisted as an independent realm until 1493 when it submitted to the Scottish king, James IV.

For many years up to 1845, when it was bought by Lord Salisbury, Rum was the property of the MacLean's of Coll. Lord Salisbury's interest in the island was as a shooting estate and he reintroduced red deer which had been hunted to extinction in the 1780s. He attempted to develop salmon fishing by diverting one stream into another but this failed when the dam collapsed. It was as a shooting estate that Rum was seen to have value and was advertised by a subsequent owner in *The Times* on 5.6.86 as ' Island of Rum. Magnificent Sporting Island on the West Coast of Scotland for sale by Auction'. John Bullough, who had been renting the shooting rights, bought the 26.000 acre island for £35,000 in 1888. He developed the sporting potential by introducing improved strains of red deer and building shooting lodges. Centuries of human habitation had stripped the island of its trees and John Bullough had 80,000 planted around Loch Scresort. Rum remained in the possession of the Bullough family until 1957 when it was sold as a nature reserve to the Nature Conservancy Council for £23,000.

The transition of Rum from an island community of three to four hundred people surviving on the cultivation of small tracts of land to a shooting estate with far fewer inhabitants was not a gradual transformation. Rum, like many areas throughout the Highlands did not escape the 'clearances', that wholesale eviction by landowners who found that sheep were more profitable than people. It could not be said in the case of Rum, where food production was unreliable, that it was a removal from any kind of idyllic existence. The dispossessed islanders, like generations of their forebears, lived in crude dwellings known as blackhouses whose interiors were discoloured by smoke from the fire having to find its way out through a hole in the roof. They had subsisted on what they could produce from lazybeds, a system of cultivation in which the meagre soil was heaped up into parallel ridges and manured with seaweed and soot-impregnated thatch. Oats and then potatoes were the main crops but in such a wet climate it was cattle and sheep that provided a more reliable source of food. During the summer the women and children took the stock up to hill pastures and lived in temporary encampments such as Airigh na mathe-innis—-'the sheiling of good grazing'. The men folk tended the crops and repaired the cottages. It was a precarious existence and William Pennant, writing in 1774, said that the people of Rum 'had famine in their looks'.

On 11th July 1826 two sailing ships, the *Highland Lad* and, bearing a name of cruel irony, the *Dove of Harmony*, came into Loch Scresort and departed for Nova Scotia taking away 300 islanders evicted by the landlord, MacLean of Coll. He had given them twelve months notice and paid the shipping company £5-15 shillings per head for their passage. Just fifty islanders were allowed to remain but that number was reduced to just one family by further evictions in 1826. The island had been let to one tenant who replaced the people with 8000 sheep. Evidence given to the Select Committee on Emigration in 1841 stated that the owner had paid his tenants a total of £600 to leave and that this had been cheerfully accepted. This contrasts with the impression of a witness to evictions, which may have been later ones by a different owner, who 'would never forget the wild outcries of the men and the heart-breaking wails of the women and children that filled all the air between the mountain shores' (quoted in *The Limping Pilgrim*. 1882 Edwin Waugh).

The resident population of Rum has never recovered from the clearances, neither sheep nor sporting pursuits requiring anything like the former numbers. Hugh Miller, in his 1857 book *The Cruise of the Betsey*, says 'The landscape was one without figures.' At its peak during the Bulloughs's time their employees and families numbered over a hundred and during the ten to twelve weeks of their annual stay would be increased by a large retinue of personal staff. These numbers declined, particularly after 1914 when Kinloch Castle became less used by the

Bulloughs. Since being taken over by the Nature Conservancy Council in 1957 the few people resident on the island have been those directly or indirectly engaged in its activities and those of its successor, Scottish Natural Heritage.

12

The Power

He traces the steam-engine always back to the tea-kettle.
Benjamin Disraeli *(of Sir Robert Peel)*

****

The fortunes of Howard and Bullough, and of the development of the whole textile industry, was dependent on steam power. In 1878, the year that production of the Rabbeth machine commenced, twelve new boilers were added to supply the increased demands for power. Advances in the design of steam engines went hand in hand with improved methods of steam raising which efficient and safe generation took a step forward in the design of the Lancashire Boiler. Instead of having just one furnace each boiler had two completely separate furnaces sitting side by side with their separate flue system. The fires are stoked at different times so that one of them is always producing maximum heat.

The ubiquitous Lancashire Boiler was still being produced and installed in many different applications up to WW2 but I was astonished to see one lying on the water in *Walden Three's* home port. Yet there it was floating serenely in the dock, distinguished from its previous industrial function by the addition of a metal hatch, a short, jaunty mast, and a tiny wheelhouse like an upended coffin. Strung to the mast a line of flags, unrelated to any maritime convention, fluttered like gala bunting. A metal plate protruded from one end of the cylinder and in the water below it a small propeller could be seen. A head appeared out of the hatch, a man emerged and clambered along the top of the boiler. There was a buzz of derisory amusement from the weekend idlers on the quay.

'He's a nutter from Accrington,' said one of them. 'Wants to sail to the Isle of Man in that.'

Had the vision of a sea voyage already been in the mind of this erstwhile sailor when one day he had come across his improbable vessel lying on the site of a demolished cotton mill? Or did the idea suddenly surface at sight of the discarded industrial hulk? Whatever process had brought him to this point I felt the need for some solidarity against this torpid crowd, scornful in their empty leisure hours of someone seeking to realise a dream, however cranky it might seem. When the man, tall and slender, in his mid-thirties, climbed up onto the quay, I stepped forward.

'I believe you are making for the Isle of Man—I know these waters well.'

The boilerman turned his large, unblinking pale blue eyes towards me: they seemed to be focussed on some distant horizon beyond my head.

'The tides can be treacherous and—' I persisted.

'She's unsinkable,' he said, moving away to adjust a mooring rope.

Going out for a few days sailing with Wallis later that week I saw that the boiler had gone. I had told Wallis of the boiler man and we were in one mind in support of his endeavour, reasoning that a person should be encouraged in the pursuit of an ambition however absurd it might appear. We headed out in a favourable breeze and the sails were nicely set when we saw it; a dark hulk on the water further down the estuary. Its owner was holding onto the mast on which a rudimentary sail flapped. When he saw us he waved urgently and our course was altered to come up to the boiler.

'My engine's overheating,' he shouted. 'I need a tow out to sea.'

We had plenty of rope and a decent engine; the ebb tide would help. Here was the chance to assist a man in achieving his dream. But I hesitated, even in the gentle waves of the estuary the boiler had a sickening roll, in the open sea the movement would be horrendous and the rag of a sail was useless. The boilerman's dream was a fantasy and could easily become a disaster. I looked at the expectant Wallis who remained silent.

'I'll tow you back in,' I shouted across.

This merciful offer was immediately rejected and we sailed away from the wallowing boiler and its solitary occupant.

'He would have been a danger to shipping,' I mumbled sheepishly.

****

Steam power came to Rum in 1845 in the form a small paddle-steamer, the *Ramsgate Packet*, bought by Lord Salisbury to transport passengers and provisions from Liverpool and to take sheep and wool to that city. The direct relevance of steam power to the island has been confined to marine applications as there do not seem to have been any steam installations on land. The most glamorous manifestation of steam power was undoubtedly the appearance of George's ocean-going yacht in Loch Cresort. *Rhouma* was an 220ft screw driven steel schooner fitted with triple expansion steam engines and had been built in Glasgow two years before being purchased by George in 1895. She was sumptuously fitted out, had a crew of thirty-eight and space for a twelve-piece orchestra.

George made several distant voyages in *Rhouma*, visiting countries as far apart as South Africa, Japan and New Zealand, and the Castle is full of furnishings and artefacts collected on these travels. Two huge bronze incense burners were a gift from the Emperor of Japan in gratitude for services in connection with the Russo-Japanese war. This war started in February 1904 with a surprise attack by the Japanese on Russian naval ships at their base of Port Arthur in China: the declaration of war, as in the case of Pearl Harbour, coming later. The Russians dispatched their Baltic Fleet on the long journey to the Far East but were denied the use of the only complete chain of coal re-fuelling stations as these were British and the country had an alliance with Japan whose naval officers had been trained by the Royal Navy. The Russians had to rely on assistance from Germany who shipped coal to the fleet as it moved round the world.

The end came with the humiliating defeat of the Russian Fleet which was annihilated in the narrow Tsushima Strait between Japan and Korea in May 1905. The Russians had taken eight months to get there and it is perhaps a reference to this ponderous progress that Accrington's steam trams of that time were commonly referred to as the 'Baltic Fleet'. It is said that the peace treaty to end this war was signed on *Rhouma* but, whilst it may have provided the location for the negotiations to take place, the actual treaty was signed at Portsmouth, New Hampshire on 5th September, 1905.

Rhouma was to be involved in another war but in a belligerent role rather than as a venue for peacemaking. George sold his steam yacht in 1911 having first had her stripped of the luxurious fittings. Some of these, a dining table and chairs, wardrobes and cupboards, were incorporated into the Castle. The purchaser was the Italian Navy who fitted her out as an armed yacht with four 6lb guns and, renamed *Guiliana*, deployed her in their war with the Turks. George replaced her with another steam yacht, *Rhouma II,* which also became an armed boat when requisitioned by the Royal Navy in 1914 and again in World War Two. George sold *Rhouma II* in 1919 and no other boats were ever registered in his name.

Another type of steam boat that would be a frequent visitor to Rum, and one in direct contrast to the luxury yacht, was the humble Clyde Puffer, the sea-going workhorse of the Western Isles. The huge quantities of masonry and building materials that had to be shipped to Rum for the construction of Kinloch Castle would be transported by these small, stumpy and rugged cargo boats which were designed with flat bottoms enabling them to be beached for unloading. The original 'puffer' was an iron canal boat on the Firth and Clyde canal in 1856. Powered by a simple steam engine with no condenser it 'puffed' at every stroke and the name stuck even when this was no longer a feature of later steam engines or when eventually diesel powered. Similar boats were developed for use beyond the canal and larger versions for the rougher sea routes to the Hebrides. This is the classic Clyde Puffer — the *Vital Spark* which featured in the Para Handy stories, and immortalised on BBC television; stories begun in 1905 by Neil Munro in his column in the Glasgow Evening News. Steam powered 'puffers' were still being built during WW2 as supply boats for the Ministry of Defence which gave them the unromantic designation of Victualling Inshore Craft. Clyde Puffers, usually diesel powered, were still in commercial operation into the 1970s.

13

The Enchantress

*Alas! The love of women! It is known
To be a lovely and fearful thing!*
Byron *Don Juan*

****

We were hoping to reach Rum by nightfall but the long passage through the Sound of Mull against contrary winds was slow and tiring. On clearing the north end of Calve Island, Tobermory, in a sudden burst of sunlight, shone like a rainbow vision, the town's colourful waterfront beckoning enticingly to weary sailors. One concurring look between myself and Wallis was enough to have *Walden Three* alter course to this Hebridean wonderland and drop anchor close to its inviting shore. Rum would have to wait.

Our mutual decision was more than vindicated when we were able to sink into foaming hot baths at a hotel known to provide for the comfort of unwashed mariners. Refreshed and glowing from a prolonged soaking I rejoined Wallis at the bar. He too was a changed man but not in a way that could be wholly attributed to soap and water. He was seated at the bar, a whisky in front of him, conversing with an unsuspected intensity to the bar attendant from whom his eyes did not waver. True, she attracted the eyes of most men in the room but with nothing like the rapt attention given to her by Wallis. He barely acknowledged my presence as I took the seat next to him.

'She's beautiful,' he breathed, when she moved off to serve someone.

There was something in the tone of his voice which presaged the prospect of trouble—trouble for the future of our voyage. When she took my order she flashed Wallis a wide, tantalising smile.

'From New Zealand—Cherie's from New Zealand,' he murmured.

'How long you staying, Wallis,' she said when she brought my beer.

'I don't know—it depends...'

'Depends on what?' she said, fixing him with her startling eyes.

'The weather,' I interjected hastily, feeling the threat of this rapidly blooming relationship.

Wallis, whose impetuous behaviour never failed to surprise, was reluctant to depart from his post by the bar and was only persuaded to return to the boat when the place became crowded and Cherie too busy to give him her special attention.

Next morning Wallis was gone, a note on his bunk said he would meet me at the hotel at lunchtime. Angry and disappointed at this delay I cursed the man and regretted ever having met him. My anger increased when there came the realisation that I would be marooned on the boat if he had taken the inflatable dinghy. But there it still was, floating alongside. The mad fool must have swum ashore—probably drowned in this chilly water. I considered continuing on to Rum alone but the boat was not equipped for single-handed sailing, certainly not for the kind of conditions likely to be met in these waters.

Wallis had survived and was at the bar—he had been given a lift ashore by the crew of a neighbouring boat. He looked sad and crestfallen—the woman had not come in to work, and I could not bring myself to be angry with the sorrowful man. But there was a compelling need to get away from Tobermory, away from that siren of a barmaid under whose spell Wallis had fallen. I mentioned, somewhat duplicitously, the possibility of returning to Tobermory on our way back from Rum and reluctantly Wallis accompanied me back to the boat. Although late in the day with the wind rising and a gale forecast, caution was literally thrown to the winds and the anchor raised. Sailing north from Tobermory we passed two rocks in the Sound of Mull, Big Stirk and Little Stirk which are referred to in the *Clyde Cruising Club Sailing Directions:*

It is said locally that if the seas are breaking on the Stirks there is a heavy sea running at Ardnamurchan [which] is completely exposed to the westward, and a very considerable sea rises in even moderate winds.

The Stirks were a mass of white foam but in my anxiety to escape from Tobermory the warning was ignored and the boat continued out towards Ardnamurchan Point, that most westerly piece of mainland Britain. On the open sea, exposed to the full blast, the wild determination to press on to Rum became fully tested. But the fates intervened and a seam in the reefed mainsail split open. Wallis, who had silently and morosely endured the constant buffeting and drenching, began to hum to himself as we came about and headed back. The wind was now shrieking through the rigging and the relief I felt on gaining the shelter of Tobermory Bay could not be denied. It would have been madness to have gone on in this weather.

The anchor had hardly taken hold before Wallis had the tender over the side. Worn out by the events of the day I declined to accompany him ashore and he disappeared into the curtain of rain sweeping across the bay. Wallis had not returned by morning and the hours passed without any sign of him. It was a day in which conditions were improving for sailing to Rum. Frequently sweeping the shoreline through binoculars became increasingly futile and only served to exacerbate my frustration. There was a strange irony in the situation that I did not wish to dwell upon—
-*Walden Three* in its symbolism of utopian dreams, stuck at Tobermory itself an embodiment of visionary intent. It was the creation of The British Fisheries Society back in 1788 in a public endeavour to establish a viable fishing industry.

The idea of going ashore and searching him out, even if I could arrange to be ferried on the tender of one of the adjacent boats, was rejected as being unlikely to bring about a positive outcome. By evening I was convinced that Wallis was not going to come back and I would not be able to sail to Rum. I might even have to leave *Walden Three* in Tobermory until able to make some arrangement for getting her back home. I cursed the man for being such a fool about a female.

It was near midnight when I was awakened by him stumbling about on deck and I found Wallis slumped in the cockpit nursing a brown paper bag.

'Whisky?' He said, holding up the brown bag.

I collected a couple of glasses and he poured out two large measures without removing the bottle from the bag. The storm had by now passed over and we sipped in silence under a clear sky. At this time of year there was no darkness, the light coming from the glowing northern horizon as if through stained glass and spreading a mysterious glow over the sleeping anchorage.

The glasses were constantly replenished. From what I could eventually gather from Wallis's fractured account he had come across another man sitting at the bar who was receiving from Cherie the treatment Wallis had believed was reserved for him alone. It was then that I noticed the bruising on his face.

'I think she must be…be some kind of…of a witch,' his speech now quite slurred.

'At least she didn't turn you into a porker,' I said.

'A pig…?'

'Circe—the goddess witch in Homer's *Odyssey*.'

We remained in that magical midsummer light until no more whisky came out of the unseen bottle.

14

The Whale

O ye Whales, and all that move in the Waters, bless ye the Lord.
Book of Common Prayer.

****

Rum was in sight, its distinctive mountain outline coming into view beyond the Isle of Muck as we rounded Ardnamurchan Point. A brisk westerly had *Walden Three* surging at times to her maximum seven knots in a lively sea. We would soon be there at this rate. Then Wallis saw the whale.

'A minke,' he shouted excitedly, leaping up onto the cabin roof with a sudden and startling exuberance.

'The binoculars,' he said, blindly stretching out a hand whilst remaining totally absorbed in watching the whale. 'Can you get a bit nearer?'

This was an imperious Wallis I had not previously encountered but his eagerness was so infectious that I readily complied with his wishes and altered course towards a black fin protruding above the surface.

'How do you know what it is?'

'The dorsal fin curving backwards—minke are fairly common in these parts --I'd been hoping to see one. Wow—my first whale.'

'It's gone,' I said.

'Don't worry, it'll surface again in a few minutes. Go more to port—she was heading that way.'

I dutifully pointed up into the wind until we were running close-hauled—-*Walden Three* apparently now had a new commander! He was right about the whale as sure enough a few minutes later a black fin appeared straight ahead along with several metres of black body.

'How big are they?' I'd heard of yachts being damaged, even sunk by such creatures.

'Nine, ten metres—weigh up to ten tons.' Wallis was still buzzing, his eyes glued avidly to the binoculars like a man hypnotised. 'They are known to leap out of the water,' His voice betraying a hope of witnessing such a performance.

There was a brief flash of white under belly as the whale submerged. At Wallis's behest we remained in the area for some time, but the whale was not seen again.

'It was a whale that made me interesting in sailing, ' Wallis told me when we were again on course for Rum . ' Moby-Dick, the white whale in Melville's book. Have you read it?'

I had to admit that it was one of those several books I was always intending to read but had never got round to it.

'It's about revenge, the white whale took off Captain Ahab's leg and his obsession with the desire to be revenged leads to disaster. Melville describes him as a man who " piled upon the whale's white hump the sum of all the general rage and hate felt by his whole human race from Adam down." If you want an example of folly, here is ultimate folly, fighting nature in this way and destroying these magnificent creatures.'

The passion that had been aroused in Wallis by our encounter with the whale seemed to have dissolved his usual reticence and reluctance to talk about himself. There had never been any occasion to press him about his personal life, shore-based existence becomes irrelevant when at sea. I knew he had some kind of civil service job in London, now I learned that he was also a published writer, although nothing I had read.

'Have you anything with you?'

'Not really—just a short story in an anthology. I brought that because it's about the sea—whales and whaling.'

At first he didn't want to show it to me but, in his still euphoric state of actually meeting a whale at sea, he was open to persuasion.

'The idea of it came after reading *Moby-Dick* and Ahab's meeting with an English whaler. That's the title—-*The English Whaler.*'

Here is what I read:

In his sleep he felt the touch of the forgiving hand of God but what was shaking him awake was the callused and untimely hand of Gabriel Mount top, First Mate of the Samuel Enderby.

'Will you rouse yourself Doctor Bunger. Sir, will you wake up. 'Tis an urgent matter.'

Jack Bunger, late of the reverend clergy, awoke slowly to his present responsibilities — ship's surgeon on a three-masted whaler in the middle of the Pacific Ocean. Muttering a liturgy of profane curses he reached for the remnants of what, an hour before, had been a rum toddy. He opened his eyes and in the gloom of his cramped quarters could just discern the First Mate's anxious face.

'Sir, would you come up on deck this minute.'

'If it's one of your rabble of a crew, Mounttop, stuck himself with a marlin spike I'll—-'

'The Captain, Doctor, he has a fearful wound.'

'The Captain! Out of my way man—-let me to him.'

The ship's surgeon, with surprising agility for someone of his round bulkiness, propelled himself from his cot and arrived on deck close behind the capable Mounttop and into the blinding glare of the fierce tropical sun and a stench of boiling blubber.

'They're bringing him aboard now,' said the First Mate, and Dr. Bunger heard the screech of rope through pulleys. Shielding his eyes, he peered over the bulwark down to a radiant sea. Swinging up towards him was the weathered face of Captain Boomer which, through the added creases of pain, grinned at his surgeon friend.

'Bunger you dog — are ye sober? I need this arm stuffed and caulked whilst there's blood still in me.'

The Captain's right arm was red with leaking blood and from the dangling hand came a constant crimson dripping down into the sea. He was swung inboard and lowered onto the blubbery deck.

It required much concentration by the doctor and involved considerable pain for his patient for the warm blood to be staunched;

each man aided by quantities of rum. Bye and bye the whole arm was wrapped in a swathe of bandages and the red stain contained.

'A great white grandfather of a whale,' the Captain told his friend. 'A bouncing great whale with a milky white head. I resolved to capture him spite of the boiling rage he seemed to be in. No sooner had I put my first harpoon in him when up looms the wide tail, vertical in the air. Down it crashes and cuts our boat clean in two leaving each half in splinters. We all struck out to escape the whale's terrible flailings. I seized hold of the harpoon sticking out of him and clung like a sucking fish. The whale went down sudden and washed me off but there was a second harpoon attached to the first by a line and as it towed through the water the barb caught me here in the shoulder. I was dragged down by the monster — down to Hell's flames I fancied but, thanks to the good God, the barb ripped its way along the length of my arm and came out. So up I floated.'

The next day the **Samuel** Enderby sailed north, its surgeon having persuaded a fevered Captain that the Equator was no place for such an ugly gaping wound to heal. The fresher winds of the North East Trades blew the whale boat's reek away to leeward but its Captain grew hotter and the smell which was beginning to fill his cabin was the one most feared by the Doctor. His round face was grave as he unwrapped the blackening wound.

'I can't save the arm,' he said. ' But I can try to save the rest of you.'

'Take the damned thing off then — I'd rather be killed by you than kept alive by any other man,' was the spirited response.'

Months later when the **Samuel** Enderby sailed into the Thames, the Captain's empty sleeve streamed out in the chilly air of a brisk north westerly like a defiant pennant.

****

'I do believe you're getting a taste for this whaling life.' The Captain was once again looking out over the whale rich seas of the central Pacific.

The ship's surgeon responded to the Captain's grin by casting his eyes up to the blackened rigging.

'Certainly not the nose for it – it's like living in the lee of a funeral pyre.'

'That hot bubbling blubber, Reverend Doctor, lights lamps in the darkest corners of England. The aroma tickling your purpled nose is the fragrant smell of money.'

Dr. Bunger watched as another chunk of flesh was hauled up onto the reddened deck. Alongside the Samuel Enderby was the remains of a large sperm whale, its hacked and peeled carcass floating in an oily pink slick. The cloudy circumstances of Jack Bunger's removal from his former office within the church had precipitated him into the occupation of ship's surgeon although he had as little expectation of saving lives as previously of saving souls. He had joined the Samuel Enderby in almost total ignorance of the peculiarities of its business. These had only become apparent on first reaching the killing ground. After his initial revulsion, not at the slaughter of God's magnificent creatures but at the stink of their boiling, he adapted well to life at sea. In a short time the smell of a whale ship at work became hardly more disconcerting to him than that of a steaming congregation on a damp Sunday.

Jack Bunger had remained with the Samuel Enderby because she was a happy, well provisioned vessel, but more essentially because of a redeeming friendship that had sprung up between him and the Captain. He had rejoined the ship for a third time in pleasurable anticipation of the Captain's cheerful companionship. Yet these blithe expectations had not been fulfilled to the extent envisaged during his lonely days ashore. True, the Captain seemed as well disposed towards him as before but there were occasions, of increasing frequency, when the ship's surgeon sensed his captain to be remote and preoccupied. The days went by without any indication to the Doctor as to the source of the Captain's troubling detachment.

He was sitting on deck in a patch of shade reading a medical text on the prevention of scurvy when his study was interrupted by a bellow from the Captain.

'What do you think of this?'

The Doctor was astonished to see a shining white whalebone thrust towards him from what had been an empty sleeve.

'It's a contraption I had the carpenter fix up for me. What do you think of it – eh?'

And smiling he swung the attached bone from side to side. Where the hand should be was stuck a wooden block like a mallet.

'It's not a proper thing at all,' said Doctor Bunger in mock disapproval. 'I'll not be associated with it.'

'A bone for a bone – scant repayment for my loss,' said the Captain flailing his new arm about him.

'Take care – you'll have my brains out with that accursed hammer.'

'That's its very purpose, Reverend Doctor, to knock sense into such solemn rogues as yourself.'

The Captain became silent, staring at his makeshift arm now motionless at his side. He turned his head and looked over the empty sea, his smile gone.

'Twelve months since that white whale maimed me – in these waters too. When I find him I'll kill the brute.'

'Is it not enough to lose one limb but you must have him chew off the others.'

'I'll be revenged for my lost arm,' said the Captain in a voice unfamiliar to his friend in its piercing vindictiveness.

'The creature was only behaving as intended by nature,' said the alarmed Doctor.

'There's a beast in me – in all men, that has its own nature. By my oath, I swear I'll have that whale,' and Captain Boomer thumped the mast with his crude wooden fist.

He registered no pain at this sharp collision of wood and bone, convincing to the Doctor of a healed stump and healthy recovery from his desperate surgery. But there was a contagion in the Captain's mind which could not be removed by a surgeon's knife. Like a rising white spectre there had waxed the deadly light of retribution. It was beginning to dominate the Captain's waking thoughts and was enacted with stark lucidity in his fevered dreams. Doctor Bunger's remonstrations had little effect other than to swell the baleful intrusion of the phantom whale into their mortal friendship. The Doctor feared a coming tragedy with his friend meeting death or further mutilation when the whale was found. Even worse, there being no monstrous *white whale except in the fevered imaginings of a man driven onto the lee shore of madness.*

****

It was a day of pressing heat and air like hot vapour. The crew were unusually silent and the normal sounds of the ship seemed strangely muffled. An uneasy expectation hung about the Samuel Enderby: *Dr. Bunger mopped his dripping face: the Captain's lost arm tingled. The horizon had vanished in an obscuring haze from out of which came a sailing ship.*

'A whaler,' announced Mounttop, the telescope clapped to his eye. 'Showing Yankee colours too.'

There was an immediate stirring throughout the ship and her deck became crowded as men gathered to watch the approaching stranger. A meeting of two whalers in remote waters was an occasion for socialising and celebration. The buzz of excited speculation grew when it was known she was a Yankee ship as American whalers had the reputation of being the most hospitable and welcoming to visitors.

Captain Boomer ordered his ship to heave-to and the Samuel Enderby *lost way and came to rest, gently lifting and dipping to the long ocean swell. The American vessel came close, rounded up smartly and immediately put a boat on the water. Dr. Bunger saw the name on the ship's stern,* Pequod of Nantucket.

'He's in a great dash to see us,' said the Captain.

The boat had pulled away from the Pequod *as soon as it hit the water. The tall, erect figure of her captain could be seen standing between the oarsmen. An unshod leg gleamed in the shimmering tropical light – a sun bleached whale bone.*

'Do you see that, Reverend Doctor,' exulted Captain Boomer. 'Bone for bone – it's becoming a regular thing.'

'Have you seen the white whale?' The grim American captain demanded of the curious faces peering down at him.

Captain Boomer lifted up his whale bone arm in affirmation and at the sight of it the American grabbed the lowered ropes and scrambled up the ship's side. The two captains stood facing one another, the eyes of each fastened on the whale bone limb of the other. What next took place the former reverend considered to be a barbarous display, offensive to civilised man. Captain Boomer thrust forward his white arm and in response the other captain raised his ivory leg. The two bones clashed and crackled together in a luminous flash. To the watching surgeon it seemed as though a spasm shook the body of his captain and he thought his friend would be taken by a fit. Captain Boomer pulled his unnatural arm away from contact with its kindred bone and a smile came to his startled face.

'Bone on bone,' he grinned. ' Boomer — and you sir?'

'Ahab,' uttered the Pequod's captain. 'Did the white whale take away your arm?'

'He was the cause of it. And that leg?'

'Aye, Moby-Dick did this to me. Have you seen the white monster hereabouts?'

'Moby-Dick you call him?'

'Have you seen him? Do you know where he is to be found?' Was the impatient and agitated response of Captain Ahab.

'I had been looking to encounter the white whale again,' said a thoughtful Captain Boomer. 'But should not such a beast be left to nature's devices. Surely, Captain, he has done us both damage enough.'

'I must have him. I will have him,' exclaimed the frenzied Ahab, his wild eyes darting about the Samuel Enderby as though expecting to discover Moby-Dick hiding on the ship.

'Steady sir, I beg you — in this heat — for the good of your health-'

'My ship's surgeon,' said the Captain in an attempted introduction, but Ahab would allow no diversion from his tormented quest.

'How long since you saw Moby-Dick? Which way was he heading?'

Captain Boomer pointed his whale bone arm. 'Last season he was swimming to the east.'

'Avast,' cried Ahab, and twisting round on his whale bone leg knocked aside the benevolent Doctor in his haste to leave.

'Is your captain mad?' asked Captain Boomer of the crewman who had accompanied Ahab on board. The man put a finger to his lips and followed his captain down into the boat. The recovering ship's surgeon and the Captain stood together watching the rigid back of Captain

Ahab as he was returned swiftly to the Pequod.

'There goes a man hot and in flames,' said the Doctor.

There was no response from the Captain who now had a faraway look in his eyes. An expression of relief gathered on his face and the corners of his mouth began to lift into a familiar smile as he looked at the Doctor.

'That man has taken my heat away. When we crossed bones it flew out of me – it cooled me and burned him the more.'

'He is a man possessed,' said the Reverend Doctor, cheered by the knowledge that the Captain was rid of his own devil and confident that their genial friendship would be fully restored. He began to hum the tune of a remembered hymn of thanksgiving as the Pequod got under way, headed east and disappeared back into a deepening haze.

15

The Castle

In Xanadu did Kubla Khan
A stately pleasure dome decree.
Samuel Taylor Coleridge *Kubla Khan*

****

From the deck of an approaching boat Kinloch Castle is clearly visible at the head of Loch Scresort but the size and extent of the building is not yet apparent, dwarfed as it is by the towering immediacy of mountains. It is placed in what was described by Hugh Miller in 1857 as 'the opening of a dreary moorland valley' (*Cruise of the Betsey*), an opinion he would no doubt amend if he were to see the scenic effect of the extensive tree planting that has taken place since his visit. From near at hand the Castle is an imposing building which is, in the context of this island, surprising in its sheer scale. Although in appearance not particularly remarkable yet it is a most visionary construction, not for any architectural distinction but because of the fantastical conception underlying its creation. This Victorian mock-castle, reflecting the royal style of Balmoral, is the physical remnant of a vanished dream, of a fervent wish to transplant an exotic world which would transform Rum into a Hebridean Xanadu.

George Bullough had the means to give uncompromising form to this extravagant desire. The only major concession he made was to reduce the length of the planned frontage of the Castle from 221ft. (the length of his yacht) to 150ft because of the two streams on the site. The red sandstone he wanted was quarried and shipped from Dumfries; the quarter million tons of soil for the extensive grounds came from Ayrshire, and many of the 300 workers were from the Accrington area. Never before, or since, has the island been the scene of such activity as during the three years of the Castle's construction. A new and temporary village was needed to accommodate the workers some of whom were accompanied by their families. Loch Scresort would be busy with boats bringing in materials and provisions and the road from the shore alive with horse-drawn carts.

An insight into George's perception of the project was the payment of an extra shilling a week for those workers prepared to wear a kilt in his newly invented Rum tartan. This bonus would have been well earned between May and September when the millions of notoriously vicious Rum midges are on the attack. The culprit, *culicoides impunctatus,* known widely as the Highland Midge, has a long standing reputation for its virulence. Edwin Waugh in 1880 described them as 'coming down in murderous hordes upon every exposed bit of skin,' and there is an ancient story of a man having been staked out naked as punishment.

The shape of this summer residence is a hollow square, reminiscent of infantry squares in the protective stance displayed against any threat to the life contained within. Turrets and castellated pediments add to the image of it being a luxurious redoubt in which to retreat from the common realities of Edwardian life. The underlying ideology of the development is the denial of natural geography by the imposition of capital and technology. Grapes, peaches and nectarines grew under large areas of glass; humming birds hovered in domed palm houses and turtles swam in heated pools. Residents could promenade without risk of exposure to the island's prodigious rainfall, safe beneath extensive colonnaded verandas. A rose garden, Italian garden, Japanese garden, rockeries and fountains transformed the surrounding wet heathland. Trees were planted in their thousands to provide a sylvan setting.

There is one particular and persistent mystery contained

72

within the Castle — there is no brother on Sir George's 'Pedigree of Bullough' displayed there beneath his Coat of Arms. Yet a child, Edward Bullough, was registered as having been born on 28th March 1880 and whose father was John Bullough, Machine Manufacturer, and the mother's maiden name was Bertha Scmidlin. This raises several questions: why did Sir George prune his brother from the family tree and how much of the rest of this genealogical map is dictated by what was thought desirable in giving the right impression rather than expressing the truth? What could it have been about Edward that caused Sir George to disown his brother?

Edward Bullough was born in Thun, Switzerland, the family home of his mother. It was at a time when it is likely that the court case was in progress which led to their marriage being annulled in 1881. Edward's early life was spent with his mother in Switzerland and later, when she remarried, in Dresden. At the time George was building Kinloch Castle, Edward, who received no inheritance from his father, was a student at Cambridge. His continental upbringing was an obvious advantage to him graduating with a degree in German and French but he had a facility for languages and went on to learn Russian, Spanish, Italian and Chinese. Edward was married in 1908 to Enrichetta Chechi, daughter of the Italian actress, Elenora Duse, who gained international fame in such roles as *Hedda Gabler* and whose performances were ranked with those of Sarah Bernhardt.

The contrasting and separate lives of the two brothers is illustrated by the different way in which each was involved in peace treaties; Sir George providing his steam yacht for negotiations of the treaty ending the Russo-Japanese War in 1905 and Professor Edward, a lieutenant with MI5 during World War 1, acting as interpreter at the Peace Treaty at Kiel in 1918. Edward remained in the academic world of Cambridge, a life in complete contrast to the goings-on at the Castle, and in 1912 became Professor Bullough. He diverged from the Bullough family characteristics in another way when, in 1923, he became a Roman

Catholic and was actively engaged in the establishment of the Roman Catholic Chaplaincy in Cambridge. His two children, a son and a daughter, each entered Dominican Orders and becoming known as Brother Sebastian and Sister Mary Mark. Edward Bullough died in 1934 but there is no evidence in Kinloch Castle of him ever even having lived.

16

The Decay

All human things are subject to decay.
John Dryden *Macfleckno*

****

The fortunes of Howard and Bullough reached their zenith in the early years of the twentieth century and it was in 1911 that Accrington's population peaked at 45,000. Wartime production during the years of the First World War obscured a situation of technological stagnation and increasing international competition. The post-war home market would also decline in the face of a developing Indian cotton industry. The response of Howard and Bullough to difficult trading conditions was to form an industrial consortium with other British companies and in 1931 Textile Machine Makers Ltd. came into being. Howard and Bullough and Platts of Oldham had the major share with 25% and 46% respectively. The combined resources of this organisation had the potential for the needed investment in technological innovation but it operated instead mainly as a cartel in attempting to control the market with restrictive practices and price fixing.

Business, and employment, at Howard and Bullough's continued to contract until once again becoming engaged in wartime production. A whole range of armaments, including aircraft components, were produced.during World War Two and employment rose to 6,000. The declining fortunes apparent in the inter-war years persisted and accelerated during the post-war period and in 1970 the Howard and Bullough name disappeared when Platt International consolidated their ownership. The workforce had by that time been reduced to 2,200. Platts were themselves taken over by an American company, Saco Lowell, in 1975 by which time fewer than 1000 were employed. The end came in 1993 when all production ceased.

Perhaps the seeds of the downfall of Howard and Bullough were sown by the untimely death of John Bullough. The loss of his inventiveness and business dynamic finding no replacement in a son whose interests and energies were directed elsewhere than the world of manufacturing. An exhibit in the Science Museum in London points to a contrasting and salutary story from Japan. Exhibited there is a 1924 Toyoda Automatic Loom, an improved model of the one invented in 1896 which had been in advance of anything else at the time. The inventor was Sakichi Toyoda whose family business produced machines for the silk industry. In the 1930s the silk industry was in decline and his enterprising son, Kuchiro Toyoda, established an automobile department within the Toyoda Automatic Loom Works and produced his first car in 1936. Toyota Motor Company — the slight change from the family name has a better sound in Japanese — is now on the verge of becoming the world's largest car company.

The 52 acres of factories which was once the extent of Howard and Bullough have, over the years, been reduced to what was the main administration and office building. After the operating business became bankrupt in 1994 the site was bought privately for residential development but Hyndburn Borough Council was keen to develop employment and training opportunities and Globe Enterprises Ltd was formed as a joint venture. People are again working here — about 1,000, no longer in the manufacture of machines, but in a hotel; restaurants; fitness and beauty businesses, and conference facilities.

17

The Plan

The present years are a period of transition,
a preparation for a new age.
A Plan For Accrington (1950)

****

The lists of war dead on local war memorials are visible evidence that in the Second World War Accrington did not suffer anywhere near the high loss of life as in the Great War. The town was also spared the scale of civilian casualties experienced elsewhere in the country and no air raids followed the nerve-tingling wail of warning sirens. The ominous drone of enemy bombers at night had other rendezvous like Manchester, whose burning was witnessed as a flickering red glow beyond the hills. One stray bomb did drop on Accrington killing the family whose home it destroyed and leaving an open gap in the terrace like that of an extracted tooth.

The imposition of a strict blackout was the main visual reminder of the country being at war; street lights were switched off, and vehicles drove with masked headlights. Bright moonlit nights destroyed the protection of darkness and gave a feeling of exposure and vulnerability. Away from home everyone carried a gasmask, the possibility of a gas attack considered highly likely in the early days and indicators of gas were placed in each locality. In the air, like inflated elephants, floated grey barrage balloons; on the ground concrete gun emplacements, emergency water tanks and street air-raid shelters appeared. Metal railings were removed to be melted down and aluminium cooking utensils collected to be used in aircraft production. The virtually traffic-free streets became safe for children's games. Shot down German planes were exhibited in the town centre and later in the war Russian Cossacks displayed their horsemanship at Accrington Stanley's football ground. The United States army, inciting considerable interest and curiosity, made its appearance when a unit was camped locally prior to the D Day landings.

The war was still being fought and V bombs were falling on London when in 1944 the Borough of Accrington appointed a Post-War Planning Committee. It was a reflection of a widespread desire to shape a future away from the stagnation and depression of the inter-war years. The strong wish for change was countywide and the 1945 election, which had Winston Churchill electioneering in Accrington, swept into power a Labour government intent on major reform. The provisions and powers of their Town and Country Planning Act gave further impetus to Accrington's forward looking approach and led to the commissioning of town planning consultants whose report, *Industry & Prudence. A Plan For Accrington,* was published in 1950. This master plan for development, one of the first for an industrial town, was radical and optimistic, fully recognising that an attractive town with modern amenities was central to successful regeneration and that 'Planning will be responsible for creating something much better and worthwhile than we have ever had in the past'.

The plan envisaged a new inner by-pass, a new bus station, and a new town hall and other civic buildings facing onto public squares. There would be a cultural area with a community centre, arts centre, swimming pool and technical school. An entertainment area of cinemas, cafes and public houses would be grouped around a new square. The blight and squalor of an earlier industrial era would be swept away; streets were to be widened, trees planted and a linear park created reaching into the town centre. It was understood that this would not all take place at once but in specific stages over time:

The future Accrington, materialising by slow degrees, here a civic building, here a new square, there a road widening, will but underline the broad continuity of democratic planning...what has been described above is the town of fifty or more years hence.

More than fifty years have now gone by since the plan was drawn up. Was the whole exercise a utopian folly, or has the folly been in the forgetting of it?

18

The Friends

And say my glory was I had such friends.
W.B. Yeats *The Municipal Gallery Re-visited*

****

On approaching Kinloch Castle the building looks solid and permanent, predominant within the space of its setting. Gone are the extensive grounds, the exotic gardens: gone with the gardeners who did not return from the Great War. But the Castle remains in outward appearance complete as ever. Yet closer inspection reveals that it too has suffered from the many years of neglect and according to reports and surveys has reached a critical stage in which its very survival is in question. The Castle's decline, as with many other aspects of British society, began in 1914. After the war Sir George seems to have lost interest in the place, visiting Rum less frequently as his life became centred on Newmarket and racing. Although still rich, he was no longer super-rich and he disposed of his steam yacht *Rhouma II*. By 1930 he was trying to let the island for sport and by 1931 he was trying to sell Rum, his half-brother Ion having already sold his Perthshire estate.

The Bullough connection was finally severed in 1957 when Lady Bullough sold Rum, including the Castle, to the Nature Conservancy Council for £23,000. Only one small piece of the island was retained by the Bullough Trust, the family mausoleum at Harris. The Sale Disposition states that the island was sold:

for the purposes of a Nature Reserve...(and the Nature Conservancy Council) agrees that, unless prevented from doing so by circumstances over which it has no control, it shall use the said island for the said purpose in perpetuity, and it shall maintain Kinloch Castle and the adjacent premises so far as may be practical to do so in the circumstances.

The new owners may well have wished that the Castle did not exist as they did not have additional funding for its maintenance. The problem was inherited by Scottish Natural Heritage which replaced the former Conservancy Council. Their 1997 Statement of Intent for Rum had as its primary management objective the restoration of the island's fertility and productivity and to increase the variety of landscape and wildlife. The difficulty presented by the Castle was clearly stated in their management plan for Rum in the period 1998-2008:

The foremost problem has always been that its maintenance fits uneasily with the functions and responsibilities of a natural heritage conservation body. Public opinion and government policy demands its conservation as a listed historic building, but no other public body has been willing to assume full financial responsibility.

Over the years there have been attempts to generate some income from the Castle: from 1976 to 1996 part of it was used as a hotel and at present it provides hostel and bed and breakfast accommodation. What maintenance has been undertaken has not kept pace with the progressive deterioration of the structure and fabric of the building through water penetration and the spread of dry rot. What seemed to be the inevitability of decay until the Castle eventually became not much more than a ruin has become less likely by the concern and actions of individuals. In 1996 George W. Randall, distressed by the state of the building, co-founded with Ewan Macdonald the Kinloch Castle Friends Association. Its main purposes are:

For the benefit of the public, to advance education and restore, preserve and improve Kinloch Castle including its furnishings and fitments...Obtain funding to carry out the restoration and preservation work. Maintain the collection of objets d'art from around the world, furnishings of the time, plus original fitments.

This initiative was not greeted with any enthusiasm by the Reserve Manager of the time who even refused permission for a notice announcing the existence of the Association to be displayed on the hostel notice board. His attitude to this development expressed in his comment 'I can not stop you forming the Association'. Things changed in 1997 when the Chairman of Scottish Natural Heritage was Magnus Magnusson and who, writing a book about Rum (*Rum: Nature's Island*), discovered that his organisation had little knowledge of the Castle and the Bullough connection. George Randall provided him with the results of his research and this led to a meeting with the Chief Executive which resulted in the formal recognition of Kinloch Castle Friends Association. In 2000 the Association became a registered charity in Scotland.

The Friends brought the Castle into national prominence by the promotion of it in the BBC TV Restoration series in which it reached the final and received 143,000 votes although missing out on the £3 million prize money for the winner. But widespread interest in the future of the Castle was created and led to the involvement of the Prince Charles' Phoenix Trust and a group of specialists being commissioned to produce a report about the options for the future of Kinloch Castle. In this report the options being considered range from continuing the existing use of the Castle but with a major restoration and repair strategy budget to the possibility of converting much of the building into residential apartments. The Kinloch Castle Friends Association prefers the option that envisages an optimum combination of different kinds of residential lettings, educational and entertainment facilities, with commercial and public access to the principal rooms.

The Castle was a friendless and inconvenient inheritance before the Association became active on its behalf. It is a small group of less than three hundred members which does not itself have any access to financial resources. Some practical help is given by its members helping to improve the grounds but it is as a pressure group that the Association has had its effect. The Castle is no longer treated as an embarrassment by Scottish Natural Heritage whose 2005 SNH press release states, 'The castle has a key role to play in the island's future'. It is hard to envisage this change in outlook having come about without the promoting efforts of the Kinloch Castle Friends Association.

19

The Restoration

Folly comes from something —
the present, yes,
we are in it,
it's the infection
of things gone.
Robert Lowell - *We Took Our Paradise*

****

There was a quiet sense of achievement in sailing into Loch Scresort and anchoring off the old jetty; the satisfaction in having successfully voyaged to our destination. Wallis stood on the foredeck silently observing Kinloch Castle and its surroundings, his eyes constantly returning to fix on the rugged heights of Hallival. He came back to the cockpit for his can of beer, a tradition on the boat when safely secured at the end of a day's sailing—-a secular, indulgent libation not to be wasted on the waters.

'This is a wild place,' he said. ' That building is a grotesque intrusion.'

'Wait until you see the inside before you make a judgement'.

I was eager to go ashore and look again on the photograph which had become etched on my memory. Once in the Castle I grew restless and impatient as the tour guide took her time in describing the interior and answering questions. It was even more frustrating and annoying as most of the questions came from Wallis. When eventually we came into the room of the photograph I was practically treading on the guide's heels. Wasn't this what I had sailed all this way for — to be reunited with the Accrington Relief Committee, to see again the picture which for me had come to symbolise the nature of Sir George's connection with the town. It was not there! I searched among the landscape paintings and portraits but nowhere in the room could I find the Relief Committee. There was a sepia photograph of a group of men — workers of some sort from an earlier period and unconnected to any relief committee. Had the photograph been removed? The guide knew nothing of it.

The remainder of the tour passed with me anxiously scanning the walls in an increasing feeling of desperation as the photograph failed to materialise. Wallis, still assailing the guide with his many queries, seemed unaware of my agitation. Had I imagined the photograph those years ago? Was this whole journey based on some fantasy of the mind? Had the vivid picture in my head no actual reality?

'The photograph isn't here,' I told Wallis as we came out of the Castle..

'Probably been put in the archives,' he said, his practical and matter of fact approach at odds with my feelings of confusion. We wandered around the outside of the Castle and back along the veranda to the front. My spirits were somewhat restored by the comforting sight of *Walden Three*, her tangible presence in the loch serving to bring some re-assurance about the whole project.

'I wonder why the photograph has been moved.'

'I expect it was giving the wrong message — the one you picked up about this expensive folly being a disaster for the town.'

' If I had never seen it we would not have made this trip.'

'I'm glad you saw it,' said Wallis, looking out towards the waiting yacht. He switched his gaze to the Castle and to the guttering where a small tree had become established.

' Nature should be left to take its course,' he said. 'This is supposed to be a reserve for nature isn't it — not run by a preservation society for stately homes.'

His outrageous suggestion took my mind away from the missing photograph. How could he not have been impressed by the Great Hall; at the furnishing of rooms almost as they were in the time of the Bulloughs; at the feminine and French elegance imparted by Lady Bullough to her apartments; at the paintings of local landscapes and the many objets d'art from around the world? At the complete cohesiveness of the place?

'How much will it cost to preserve this place?' was his response.

I told him of a report prepared in 2003 which estimated that about £5,500,000 would be needed for the Castle's repair and conservation.

'Likely to turn out to be double that—it's not worth it.'

'Prince Charles' Phoenix Trust has become involved,' I said.

'That's supposed to be concerned with the regeneration of communities—the money would be better used on regeneration back in Accrington. There would be some historical justice in that.'

For someone who had never been to Accrington I thought that Wallis's argument was becoming rather rarefied.

'It exists, it's here, it's solid.' I slapped my hand on the Castle's red sandstone.

'That rock is alien to the island,' he said..

The dreaded midges were now at work and we lost no time in getting back to the boat. The great advantage of living on a boat in these parts is that the creatures do not follow you across the water.

'It would be such a loss,' I said, when we were settled on board and looking back over the loch to the Castle.

'Of what? A mock castle in an uninspiring Scots Baronial style—it has no real architectural merit.'

'But the collection— the beautiful interior?'

'Granted it has more style inside than outside. The contents? I didn't see any paintings of distinction and most of the objects are of the sort any wealthy round-the-world tourist of the time would have picked up. Although I did see a splendid Japanese bronze incense burner— far superior to any of the other stuff.'

'Wallis, you are judging the place by its individual components—its uniqueness is in its totality, in the Castle's completeness and historical significance.'

'It's a monument to huge wealth, ego and acquisitiveness which shows little taste or discrimination. Kinloch Castle is a relic of Edwardian class divide. Look how cramped and basic are the servants' quarters in sharp contrast to the lavish provision for the family and guests. And that ballroom with high windows to prevent the staff from observing the antics of the Bulloughs and their society guests. Even the drinks had to be passed through a cupboard in a way that avoided visual contact by one of the lower orders.'

Not since the whale had I seen Wallis so impassioned, although now it was expressed in feelings of angry disapproval rather than joyful excitement. He was too incensed to remain seated and rose, going forward to the bow where he made some unnecessary adjustments to the anchor chain.

'It's a listed building—Category A,' I persisted when he returned aft. 'Considered of national importance.'

'To which nation—it's an English parody of Scottishness,' his fire had not gone.

'People come to see it; it's one of the attractions of the island.'

'The country is littered with stately homes. Rum's real attraction is its wildness. This kind of wilderness is a rarity.'

'Even visitors wanting to experience wilderness need accommodation and there's little elsewhere on Rum.'

'For a fraction of the money spent on the Castle they could be accommodated more comfortably in a new eco-friendly building— built from materials here on the island.'

'So you would just leave the Castle to decay?'

'It would be a dynamic ruin—nature at work reclaiming the place'

'And let the collection rot?'

'Plenty of museums would take and display anything of interest. The Castle and its contents could be digitally recorded and preserved in virtual reality.'

'Wallis—I didn't realise you were such a vandal'

'The whole country is in danger of preserving unworthy building in a mass hysteria of undiscriminating nostalgia.'

It was time for a dram. There was no disagreement about the whisky as we sat in silence warmed by the mellow liquid. The Castle glowed in a brief burst of sunlight, unaware of the problems its presence was causing.

20

The Return

Home is the sailor, home from the sea.
Robert Louis Stevenson

****

What is it about the return leg of a journey that has such a different feeling to it? Something more than approaching the same places from a new angle. Even the same maps and charts seem to take on a new significance—are seen with a changed eye. More than anything there is a shift in what is hoped for and of there being different expectations. A voyage out has the excitement of anticipating new experiences and the possibility of realising some desire which generate an enlivening feeling of optimism. A different sensibility comes into play when retracing one's steps and even on a circular route around the world on a steam yacht there must have come a point when there was a feeling of being homeward bound. Returning to the already known and familiar life does not have the daring force of discovery and a safe and expeditious journey home becomes a major consideration. That is perhaps why, after leaving Loch Scresort and turning south, *Walden Three* was now no longer at sea but passing between fields and beneath overhanging trees as she puttered gently along the Crinan Canal. Wallis was coming to the end of his leave and could not afford to be delayed by the uncertainties and perils of returning round the Mull of Kintyre and this canal was built precisely to avoid that route.

Still having some anxiety about the goddess in the hotel bar at Tobermory I had impressed on Wallis the attractions of going by way of the famous island of Staffa and visiting the holy island of Iona and so had avoided the Sound of Mull and its temptations. There was so much I didn't know about my sailing companion or his other life. One thing that I did learn about Wallis was that he had experience of operating locks and enjoyed this activity. An extremely useful capability on a canal that managed to include fifteen of them within its nine mile length. My main concern in the canal was to prevent *Walden Three* from being damaged by the rough masonry of the lock walls, the builders of the canal back in 1801 having little perception of the vulnerability of a modern yacht's paintwork.

Would the Bullough family and their visitors to Rum have come through this canal? Wallis wanted to know. Quite possibly, I told him, and certainly it would have provided the fastest route for supplies and provisions from Glasgow before the coming of the West Highland Railway. This did not arrive at Fort William until 1894 and, in one of the last major railway projects in Britain at that time, only reached Mallaig in 1901. The transformation of Mallaig from a small community of crofter/fishermen to a major fishing port taking place at the same time as the building of Kinloch Castle. Even in those days the economic advantages of subsidised rail travel was acknowledged as from the start the line was dependent upon Government support.

There was a sense of freedom from the confines of canal travel and the effort of working through locks as we nosed out into the sea again at Ardrishaig. It was a freedom not without its own particular difficulties. Short of time we had to press on and were sailing through the night on alternate watches, one of us at the helm whilst the other slept. I came up to relieve Wallis and saw that we were running before a brisk north-westerly with a following sea, in the darkness the waves seen only briefly before the boat was lifted by the stern and propelled forward as they passed under. A larger wave, its crest a white gleam in the darkness, broke over the stern filling the cockpit and drenching us both.

'It's getting worse,' said Wallis, as he went below.

The next few hours were spent concentrating on preventing the boat from being slewed broadside to the waves and knocked over but by the time Wallis re-appeared the wind had eased and the sea was less threatening. He looked around in the general gloom where no stars shone and to the one bright patch of illumination.

'Sellafield,' I said. 'It's a brilliant landmark.'

'Not a nuclear folly then?'

'That too, perhaps. I suppose what's a folly depends on your point of view.'

'Precisely,' said Wallis, with a broad grin, as though welcoming me to an opinion he had already arrived at.

It was a weary crew that tied up the salt-stained *Walden Three* when we finally docked. Wallis had to dash off to catch his train home but as he was leaving he had one last surprise. He told me he had developed a strong desire to visit that singular town, Accrington.

21

The Confessions

The truth is rarely pure, and never simple.
Oscar Wilde

****

It is not easy to separate fact from fiction: the real from the imagined. Even accounts and events presented as factual, unless based on direct personal experience, are dependent upon the veracity and accuracy of their sources. Shared experiences are recollected differently and time distorts and erodes individual memories. What can be clearly identified are the imaginative and fictitious aspects of a story. The time has come to confess to these.

There was no boat named *Walden Three*; true there was a sailing boat but it retained its pre-existing name. Changing the name of a registered boat is not simply a matter of painting over the old one. This sliding away from an original intention was in itself symbolic of the departure from some abstract philosophical concept of living that the boat was expected to embody and into the engrossing actuality of sailing. The reality of life afloat determined by the physical activity required in sailing and maintaining a seaworthy craft. The relevant literary influences coming from the reading of nautical almanacs and navigational guides: any intellectual activity directed towards the interpretation of Admiralty Charts and spiritual sentiment expressed in the hushed reverence devoted to the intoned liturgy of the Shipping Forecast.

The boat never reached the Isle of Rum, the nearest it came was just beyond Tobermory when forced back into shelter by a gale. It had not even been heading for Rum as my first visit to the island had yet to take place. The eventual sailing to Rum was not strictly speaking in my own boat but in a yacht I had chartered, *Walden Three* having been sold. Neither was there a Wallis, who is a fictitious character though perhaps exhibiting some of the quirks of different sailing companions. It was the author who caught the chicken in Turkey. Wallis's adventure with the Tobermory barmaid is an inflated development of a situation which involved one of the sailing companions. To believe that there is such thing as pure fiction would be almost as big a folly as to think that biography is devoid of it.